of it Dr X hadn't been too clever about those either, simply telling her, more – or, rather less – diet, and it stood to reason little bits of food for a long time came to the same thing as lots of food for a short time, which was what *she* believed in, Nature's Way Was Best, no wonder she was always craving for chocolates if she should be eight feet high . . .

Furthermore (claimed Mrs A), she attended every surgery Dr X held, as well as calling him to her house several times a week, to enable him to keep in touch with her case, but he showed no real interest; that was the trouble with Capricornians, no sympathetic planetary vibrations. Nor did his weighing-machine give out little cards, at least not to panel patients it didn't, but what could you expect from a doctor who announced that until the zodiacal significations could give him three in a row at Newmarket, a horoscope for him was what he looked down ears with . . .

Dr X said in reply that from the way his weighing-machine had got countersunk into the floor, he thought Mrs A's sign should be Libra, lucky stone the gall-stone. He admitted failing to reduce her weight and invited suggestions for dealing with a woman whose usual elevenses consisted of a pound-and-a-half of chips and a bottle of invalid port, and who, because her pills were labelled "before meals", always insisted on taking a meal after them. He added bitterly that he'd missed the big race at Kempton Park and whatever the Minister's, the chairman's, the clerk's, or Mrs A's zodiacal signs might be, on this occasion Taurus was certainly in the ascendant . . .

Both parties then withdrew and the Chairman announced he was sure the stars foretold they'd be able to fine Dr X pretty heavily for something or other, if it was only that last crack, and at least it would help to pay for the damage Mrs A had done to the lift.

THE Roman legionaries did a lot of marching. How did they cope with athlete's foot? History doesn't relate. But, some years ago, I wondered whether the explanation lay in the olive oil they anointed themselves with after the baths to which they were so passionately addicted. Public baths must even then have harboured the fungus. I had had this pestilential affliction since my boarding-school days, and had run the gamut of all the recommended remedies, with the result that I had come to agree with the definition of a skin disease that Russell Howard used to give at the London Hospital. "A skin disease," he used to snort, "is a name and an ointment. The patient never dies and never gets well." Well, about four years ago I took a leaf from the Romans. After my bath each morning I rubbed a drop or two (no more) of oil between my toes, leaving the thinnest film. I haven't had a recurrence since then, and some of my sceptical colleagues now agree that old Dr Peripatetic may be on to something. How the cure works is uncertain. It may keep the skin from becoming sodden. One thing is certain, anyway – there are no side-effects, and no-one is going to report five years from now that the olive oil upset the serum-globulins or caused an antoimmune reaction.

NINETEEN years ago this month I raked out the glowing embers of our last camp fire on the shore of Elterwater. Tom was packing up the tent; George was gazing wistfully at the cloud patterns across the Langdale Pikes; Dick was fully occupied behind the wall. The ink was drying on our names in the Medical Register, the Final carbuncles were fibrosing nicely in divers places, and an eager world lay waiting.

That Arcadian climax of six years' comradeship and academic tribulations was shattered by the crackling exhaust of an MG swirling down the lane. A pair of silk stockings swung over the side and we were driven away to the sweet bondage of medicine and matrimony. A lot of queer things have happened since then. Tom packed up his tent for the last time in the Western Desert; George can still see the outline of Dungeon Ghyll in the haze of his Midland factory chimneys. Dick has graduated to a thunderbox in Rhodesia. I am left to worry whether the Medical Register has lost us, how far away is the final coronary, whether there is time to catch up with the world.

The silk stockings have changed into nylons, the nymph MG has metamorphosed into the sedate imago of a family saloon. Matrimony's sweet bondage has yielded the fruits of our labour in the shape of a trio of teenagers, whose genes have stored some mysterious memory of wood smoke and fresh bracken. The camp-fire ashes on the shore of Elterwater have smouldered on into the hearts of the next generation, fanned into flame by the breezes of adolescence, and threatening once more to burn the fingers of our middle age. The family have demanded to be taken camping.

From the darkest recess of the lumber-room we unearthed a couple of tents. The moths and the mice and the mildew betrayed the neglect of nineteen years' callous disregard for the wind on the heath. Yet as the once-white tented little hell, still titled "Pitz Palu," was unfolded on the lawn, a wave of nostalgia swept across the years. I saw it once more pitched on the cliffs of Devon, on the foothills of Snowdon, in the mists of Sligachan on Skye. Strange that those memories should linger when the more fantastic bivouacs of war are thankfully forgotten.

The cupboard in the garage yielded up the primus. I burnt my fingers more than metaphorically instructing the family how to work the flaming thing. The running commentary was almost back to the uninhibited standards of medical student days. The parental example of Swiss Family Robinson was sadly missing. The Queen Bee has collected an enormous pile of blankets, eiderdowns, and cushions, upon which I have heaped scorn but secretly slipped in a couple of camp beds. It is asking a lot of anyone's iliac crest to nestle fourteen stone on a rocky field. The family are now heaving it all into the luggage locker of the car, and the back end is down on the springs. The camp fires will be burning again tonight and nineteen years are rolling away.

# IN ENGLAND NOW

*The Peripatetic*

Nathaniel Dance, RA (1734–1811)

Presented to *The Lancet* in June, 1961, by Dr N. M. Goodman "on concluding his first 250 published contributions to the journal".

The original Peripatetics were pupils of Aristotle, and the name derives either from their master's habit of walking about while teaching or from a covered walkway in the Lyceum in Athens.

# IN ENGLAND NOW

Fifty Years of Peripatetic
Correspondence in *The Lancet*

Selected and edited by
G. A. C. Binnie
R. L. Sadler
W. O. Thomson
D. M. D. White
D. W. Sharp

LONDON: *The Lancet*/Hodder & Stoughton

British Library Cataloguing in Publication Data
In England now.
  1. Medicine
  I. Binnie, G. A. C.
  610

  ISBN 0-340-51405-1

Published by *The Lancet*/Hodder and Stoughton,
Mill Road, Dunton Green, Sevenoaks, Kent TN13 2YA.
Editorial Office: 46 Bedford Square, London WC1B 3SL.

Photoset by Rowland Phototypesetting Limited,
Bury St Edmunds, Suffolk

Printed in Great Britain by T. J. Press (Padstow) Limited,
Padstow, Cornwall

# CONTENTS

*This book is dedicated to the authors of the contributions, included herein or not, who have delighted Lancet readers since September, 1939.*

*The drawings are by Albert Rusling.*

# PREFACE

WITHOUT fanfare *The Lancet* opened up its column In England Now in September, 1939, with the phrase "Happening to Guy's yesterday . . .". What followed was a correspondent's concern that an air-raid shelter being constructed at that London teaching hospital, lacking urinals, might not be too hygienic. A "sandbag mentality" of improvisation and adaptation pervaded the column in the war years that gave it birth. Dr Stephen Taylor (later Lord Taylor of Harlow), in a brief spell on the journal, introduced IEN with the purpose of showing how British medicine was coping with the war. In the first two weeks news came in from London, Oxford, Liverpool, Bristol, and Cardiff. It had to be a Merseysider who was overheard by a peripatetic saying "I'll tell you what I'd do to Hitler. I'd do what they did to Napoleon – send him back to St Helen's." Post-war the column changed; contributions became shorter and funnier but the essential ingredients of wit, wisdom, and humanity remain.

*Lancet* editors despair when told by their readers "Of course, I always turn first to In England Now." What follows is an edited selection from half a century of contributions. To *Lancet* readers whose favourites are not here I can only express the hope that the loss is made up for by pieces you have not come across before. Newcomers to the column begin here . . .

Editor, *The Lancet*

# I

# Under Siege, 1939–45

I HAD just emerged from a farmhouse and was thrusting my obstetric forceps into my hip pocket, when I was startled by loud backfiring. Looking up I saw an aeroplane circling as though the pilot intended to land. "By the holy smoke!" I exclaimed, "It's a Nazi!" While trying to make up my mind which way to run, I saw a splash of white appear in the sky, and thereafter my attention was about equally divided between the plane and pilot, suspended by his parachute, floating gracefully towards me. In a flash I realised my awful predicament. Here was I about to face the Nazi hordes – or one of them, at any rate – in a state of physical exhaustion after delivering the farmer's wife. I remember thinking: How like the Nazis, always catching their opponents at a serious disadvantage!

I ran back into the house, changed into the boots (I always keep in my obstetric bag a pair of mountaineering boots with spikes in the soles), and snatching a pitchfork from a corner of the kitchen rushed out to do battle. I raced down the garden path, scrambled through a privet hedge, and there I saw the scoundrel thirty yards away rolling over on the ground. I ran up to him, panting for breath, but managed to splutter, "Who are you?" I don't know what I expected him to say, but his reply took my breath away – or what was left of it. "I'm a German airman and a gentleman," he said haughtily. I was relieved to observe that he showed no inclination to be truculent, and I felt increasingly embarrassed by my pitchfork. However, this problem solved itself a moment later, for the wind blew the parachute

1

cords around my legs, and hopelessly entangled I fell in a heap in the grass. Mercifully the pitchfork dropped well out of the reach of either of us. But as I landed squarely on my hip I let out a yell of pain. "It's those — forceps," I howled, withdrawing the battered instruments from my hip pocket, while the German looked at me in consternation. "I see no blood," he remarked. "I was speaking idiomatically," I explained loftily, "you would not understand." "I know," he suddenly exclaimed beaming, "you are a doctor!" I nodded assent, ruefully massaging my right buttock. "That is good," he said, "can you tell me how far I am from the Royal Faculty of Physicians and Surgeons of Glasgow? I am tired of the Nazis. I am a refugee. Soon after the war started I decided to be a doctor. Therefore I come to Glasgow to take the triple qualification. That is the best medical qualification in the world is it not so? Already I have my first examination passed, including the materia medica, and I know the Pharmacopoeia Britannica." I decided to test the truth of what he said by quizzing him. "What is the dose of hydrarg. cum cret.?" I asked. "Grains 1 to 5," came the prompt reply. "Well," I said half apologetically, "it's not a long step from hydrarg. cum cret. to Hitler cum Crete; tell me, what is going to be the next move in the eastern Mediterranean?" "The next German offensive will begin on . . ." Here our conversation was rudely interrupted by the Home Guard who seemed to have popped up out of the soil.

I was looking forward to the broadcast that followed a few days later, but in the middle of the news bulletin I was called to the surgery. When I returned I found my wife helpless with laughter. "Was it as funny as all that?" I inquired rather nettled by this reaction to what must surely have been one of the most remarkable incidents of the war. "Darling," she replied, "I've told you scores of times that you really must get a new suit and a new hat . . . Of course, I should have recognised your voice *anywhere*, but the BBC actually described you as a ploughman!"

How widely is this column read, how far afield it travels! On one occasion, in 1940 it was: I had been lamenting the national lack of policy regarding tuberculosis during the early days of the war. Concerning the inevitable increase in its incidence I wrote: "It is true that quite advanced cases of pulmonary tuberculosis are being passed into the Army so long as they present no stethoscopic signs, and that a number will perish in military hospitals; but against them, thousands of consumptives have been evacuated from their sanatoria to tenements hermetically sealed during the hours of blackout, where they are sowing the infection quietly and efficiently . . ." Strong words? Yes, but in their context, obviously satirical. But they didn't sound at all satirical, they sounded perfectly frightening (to me, at any rate) when quoted practically word for word the following night by Lord Haw-Haw.

My house surgeon, a tough South African, was having supper with us. We were talking of boxing, for which he had won many prizes, when he threw out the remark, "I originally took up boxing at school to defend my young brother George." Sensing a story I pressed him further, and this is what he told me. While the other boys at school were reading thrillers and adventure stories young George would be busy with his sewing. Naturally he came in for more than his share of ragging. Hence the boxing. One day, when he was not quite sixteen, one of the masters called him a young so-and-so. George straightaway packed his bag and disappeared. No trace of him could be found for six weeks, when his parents ran him to earth in a second-rate lodging-house earning a living by taking in dressmaking. Neither blandishment nor threat could induce him to abandon this life, much to the disgust of his father, a stalwart veld farmer. A few months later the family were startled to see in bold headlines in the local paper "Ex High-school Boy Wins £1000 Dress Designing Competition". Young George had set his foot on the ladder to fame. This time his father arranged to send the boy to Britain to learn his trade thoroughly, and in a few years George was chief designer to a firm whose name is a household word in fashionable circles in London, Paris and New York. But now he is in the RAF, and in charge of a heavy bomber. On the way home from a bombing raid young brother George hands over to the second pilot while he gets on with his embroidery. Apparently he no longer needs a protector.

HE was a badly wounded Cockney who had arrived in soiled battledress that had not been off for three weeks. He had been washed and fed, his wounds had been dressed and he was lying comfortably between clean sheets, reading a newspaper. The Red Cross had provided him with soap, a flannel and a toothbrush, while our generous American Allies had given him cigarettes and a slab of chocolate. He had even been visited by the mayor complete in his gold chain. I asked him how he was. "Alright," he said, "but I never did 'old with these places, not since I 'ad me tonsils out as a nipper. I'd sooner spend a week in a slit-trench full of water than a night in an 'orspital." I wonder how many people get a lifelong horror of hospital from having their tonsils out as a nipper.

ONE night one end of the nurses' home was wrecked by a bomb, but happily they were all over at the hospital, most of them doing voluntary duty admitting casualties. The next day one of them received a wire from her father in the country: "Have heard the news pack everything and come home." She wired back: "Nothing left to pack not coming."

3

I HAD been working late in casualty and managed to get the last seat on the only late-night bus. By the time the conductor came several people were standing. He counted them and announced, "We've one too many. Last one on gets off." Nobody stirred. "I'll get the driver." The driver peered down the crowded bus: "I'm not starting this bus until somebody gets off', he said. Driver and conductor stood on the kerb waiting, but no-one moved. The conductor came into the bus again, by this time quite belligerent, and announced, "If nobody gets off, me and my mate's going for a policeman." Some time after they had left, the sound of running footsteps echoed across the empty bus-station, and a young man came panting into the bus. "Phew!" he gasped, "I thought I'd missed it." He had scarcely got his breath back when the conductor and driver returned with a policeman. The policeman stepped onto the platform. "Nar-then, nar-then," he said, firm but conciliatory, "there's one passenger too many in this bus and the last one on has got to get off." The young man knew that he was the last to get on. "Alright," he said, "I'll get off, but you'd no need to bring a policeman." The policeman looked quietly satisfied, the driver climbed into his cab. The conductor's face relaxed, he rang the bell, and off we went. Nobody said anything, but, of course, it was wartime and we all knew how dangerous careless talk could be.

"Now," said the examiner in first aid to the local Lancashire candidate, "what would you do for a case of strychnine poisoning?" "Ah'd gie 'im starch," was the answer. "Now just think again," said the examiner. The local looked baffled, and his next-door neighbour whispered to him, "Tha's thinking of iodine poisoning." "By gum, ah am an' all," grinned the local, "if ah gave 'im starch, it 'ud nobbut stiffen 'im!"

THE school doctor was examining evacuees. As two boys were shown into the room he took one glance at them and then his face lit up as he exclaimed: "Aha, twins!" One of the boys disdained any reply, merely sniffing and wiping his nose on the back of his hand. The other, with a look of contempt, said flatly: "No, we're *not* twins." The doctor, palpably deflated, motioned to the boys to be seated while he took their names and addresses. Having finished this, he stood up with a look of triumph on his face. "I told you so!" he exclaimed, "You're as like as two peas; you have the same birthday; and you have the same father and mother. You're twins." "No, we're *not* twins," said the more talkative one emphatically. "Well, what are you?" demanded the doctor irritably. "We're all that's left of triplets."

4

HE pulled off his shirt in the consulting-room and there was the scar I had not set eyes on for eighteen years. His face had seemed vaguely familiar as he walked in for his insurance examination, but I plead the excuse that it was upside down and a lot less pink when I last saw it emerge from my anaesthetic mask, trolley-bound back to Side-ward K. So that was who he was, the only British officer I ever knew to be bayoneted by his own side.

He was a stocky little chap and what he lacked in inches he made up in guts and self-confidence. He had his own peculiar contribution to make to Britain's war effort. He specialised in unarmed combat. Those seasons as scrum-half behind a famous pack of forwards had not been spent in vain. Brawn had writhed before brains in many a friendly, and what he could do to the enemy was a much valued factor in our war potential. So much so that he was selected to lead a circus of unarmed combatants giving demonstrations of his art. The most popular turn was to pick out the beefiest-looking private soldier from the spectators, and invite him to do his worst with a fixed bayonet. A quick side-step by the expert, an even quicker tug on the weapon, and another astonished gladiator went base over apex. So it went on until some brass-hat had the bright idea of showing the Army's prowess to the Home Guard. Off went the circus to deepest Somerset. The theory of unarmed combat was expounded, and then the stooge was picked for the fun. He took up his rifle, fumbled the bayonet into place, and stood ready with a most unsoldierly guard. The first attack was honours even: neither party made contact. The second was just too easy. A lazy curving swing with a terminal flick nicely hooked the instructor from any further part in the proceedings. "'Twas simple," remarked the Home Guardsman, "Oi bain't using a pitchfork all me life for nothin' – 'twas just he doan't know proper way to keep hisself clear at haytime."

IN the days of the air-raids patients in our hospital were all issued with basins. The idea was that they would hold these basins inverted over them throughout the period of danger and thus ward off broken glass. But now this plan has been abandoned, largely because of one odd old man. He came in out of a taxi, and forthwith went pleasantly crazy. He would walk out of the ward in pyjamas on the ground that he had a dinner engagement, sit up in bed and applaud vigorously from the front row of the stalls; once, to a doctor who inadvertently remarked that he was bats, he replied "Ce n'est pas moi, c'est toi." Naturally he received his basin like everyone else, at the hands of our sweetest nurse. Imagine her shame and horror when she heard the echoing sounds of an old man urinating into it. She ran back. "No, no," she said. "It's not for that. It's to put on your head." And with a look of surprise he immediately put it there.

A NEUROLOGIST and a psychiatrist were appointed medical officers on a troopship going to the East. The inevitable happened in the Indian Ocean, when a pleasant game of bridge was interrupted by a summons to a soldier with a perforated peptic ulcer, so obvious that even we could diagnose it. The other doctors aboard, all psychiatrists, were consulted and none of us had ever opened the abdomen. By good fortune there was a nurse aboard who knew which bits of string to use, and which needles and instruments were least likely to be dangerous. Anaesthesia was induced by one psychiatrist – "Pentothal" and open ether. So much ether had to be used owing to the high temperature that the navigating officer on the bridge some decks above said he felt quite sleepy. The neurologist was surgeon and was told what to do by a psychiatrist. After some scratching about through an unorthodox incision, the small intestine appeared. By means of cutting various unidentified structures a fine view of the stomach and duodenum was obtained and a small perforation found. The word "purse-string" seemed familiar, the technique less so; however, the perforation was finally closed. Closure of the wound was difficult, but with any luck a postoperative hernia was prevented because everything was stitched to everything else. Only three swabs were used, so the counting of these was easy (strange memories of the piles of swabs and elaborate counting technique of the orthodox surgeon). The patient made a remarkable recovery; and when disembarked three days later was fitter than any postoperative perforation which we had seen (our experience was admittedly limited).

The nurse's remark at the end – "It is easy to see you are not really surgeons; you are far too polite."

GRANDMA was right after all. How we used to laugh when she told us not to sit on cold stones, and when she made grandpa wear his cholera belt! But we three, sceptical and up to date as we are, have had our illusions rudely shattered in a spasmodically painful and gripping fashion. On a recent luxury cruise in the tropics, as guests of the Royal Navy, we enjoyed rushing from our overheated mess to the moon-drenched upper deck, to dry our sweat-swodden shirts in the balmy breeze. When next we met, at 0500 hours – much earlier than expected, and ere the rising of the sun – we were candidates for one seat, and in this three-cornered contest precedence was taken in order of seniority. A colonic catastrophe had overtaken us. In vain we assayed to ascribe the cause to things bacteriological, or dietetic; Dame Nature had sneaked up on us. Chill had seized us in her icy grasp, and our vitals, not our victuals, were violently involved.

THE lady of the manor was entertaining a party of Czech airmen, and one of them happened to make some remark about his wife. "Have you any family, then?" said the lady. "Family? What is that?" "Have you any children?" "No, we have no children; it is a great grief to us – you see, my wife, she is unbearable." One of his fellow Czechs laughed heartily. "He do not know how to speak proper English," said this officer "what he mean is that his wife is inconceivable." A third Czech laughingly joined the conversation. "No, no, what they mean, madam, is that his wife is impregnable."

English manners have long been a mystery to the foreigner. André Maurois, for example, says that in France it is ill-mannered to let a conversation die, whereas in England if you say nothing for two or three years people begin to think what a nice quiet fellow that Frenchman is. The best example of our national manners I have ever seen was displayed under my nose last Saturday. The carriage was full, the train had begun to move, when the door opened and in leapt three spirited WAAFs. The largest made straight for the opposite door of the carriage and tried to open it. The train was now moving at 20–30 mph and the soldier sitting in the corner said with some (but not much) astonishment: "Do you want to open the door?" "Yes," replied the WAAF, "I do." Nobody said a word. We watched with keen but silent interest as the soldier drew back the stiff latch for her and pushed the door open. "Oh," said the WAAF, unshaken. "I thought it was a corridor train. You can shut it up again." Silently the soldier shut the door; and my national manners which had stood up so well to the strain suddenly deserted me. "That was uncommonly obliging of you," I said to the soldier. "Well," he answered reasonably, "I thought perhaps she wanted to commit suicide."

A Berlin surgeon, desirous of demonstrating his new sigmoidoscope to a visitor, followed the old German custom of seizing the nearest outpatient, and, disregarding her protests, passed the instrument. When the examination was over he discovered that she wasn't a patient but only a visitor. However, the tale has a true Teutonic ending, for on being informed that the demonstration of a new instrument to a foreigner was for the greater glory of the Reich, the temporary patient said "Heil Hitler" and was well pleased.

# II

# Colleagues

THE animus between the two senior surgeons in our hospital is legendary. They pass each other in the corridors with the barest of nods; and stand, back to back, drinking tea at staff meetings. How it all started no one knows. There are rumours of intense competition for the undergraduate medal in surgery, which neither won; rivalry over a beautiful model, who later married a psychiatrist; and an argument over whose name should come first in their only, non-published, joint research paper. But it is mostly conjecture. Some of their verbal exchanges have become hospital folklore:

"May I give you a hint on how to improve your stitching technique?"
"If you must."
"Try to be a little more careful."
or
"Is that my overcoat?"
"As to that I cannot say. It is certainly the one you were wearing when you came to the meeting tonight."

The final nail in the coffin of their fragile fraternisation arose out of a domiciliary visit. One of them had been assiduously attending a wealthy patient for a rumoured exorbitant reward. Owing to a breakdown in communication he could not be contacted when needed urgently. In desperation, his rival was summoned. An indwelling catheter had blocked. The replacement took but a few minutes and after a glass of excellent sherry, a chequebook was discreetly produced. He was asked to name his fee. The opportunity was too good to miss. "Well," he said, "It was an emergency and prompt action was certainly needed. The procedure was not without difficulty and I have been inconvenienced to some extent by having to drop everything to stand in for my colleague who is, no doubt, engaged upon more important matters. Now let me see, would a pound be too much to ask?" They say that blood was almost shed when next they met.

OUR new surgeon, Mr Y, is proof that the old breed of consultant is not, as many feared, extinct. He is terse and outspoken and does not believe in words such as please or thank-you. Resentment burns behind many a starched apron. As a psychiatrist I find that one of my unofficial roles is to lend a sympathetic ear to disgruntled nursing staff.

I gathered that Mr Y had been causing trouble. Sister was laying up a trolley with more banging and crashing than was either necessary or desirable. He had commented on the lack of preparation shown in two of her patients he had sigmoidoscoped. Judging by the quantities of hot soapy water and the lengths of rubber tubing Sister was flinging around, it seemed likely that there would be no cause for complaint when Mr Y 'scoped Mrs Z on the ward tomorrow. I counselled caution, but in vain. By the time Mr Y and his entourage arrived the next morning, Mrs Z contained more soapy water than a launderette – no one had dared tell Sister that, contrary to all natural laws, what had gone up had not, as yet, come down.

Mr Y prides himself on his dress, and his light grey suit that morning was a model of sartorial excellence. An underling inserted the apparatus into the correct place and stood aside. The consultant eye was appplied to the lens. Mr Y grew angry. Despite all he had said, Mrs Z's rectum was full and he could see nothing. He removed the eyepiece and threw it into a kidney dish, leaving the rest of the sigmoidoscope in situ, and proceeded to dress Sister down. A low rumbling from Mrs Z passed unheeded. Then there was an explosion. A rectum full of faeces and soapsuds, finally insulted by cold steel, rebelled, expelling with force its entire contents down the tube, which acted like a gun barrel. Mr Y was right in the line of fire.

THE other night in the contemplative peace of my bath I was tempted to produce the following definitions:

A Physician is a chap who is prepared to diagnose a condition that he did not know existed.

A Surgeon is a chap who knows that if he can't cut it out it isn't there.

WHEN Giles and I were young house-officers, a combination of leave and illness left us in sole charge of the medical wards for a weekend. The departing registrar reassured us that all was well. There was no need to worry. "All except that chap in the corner," he said. "I don't know what it is but I have an uneasy feeling about him." And, indeed, later on that night the patient went into rigors. Giles and I looked on, puzzled and helpless, as the nursing team settled him down. The night sister, long in experience, took us aside. "Look, boys," she said, "I was talking to him a little while ago and he has been in Korea. I wonder if it is malaria?" We both brightened up considerably. I took off some blood and we proceeded to the laboratory. "What do we do now?" I asked. Luckily one of the technicians was working late and he showed us how to stain the blood smear. We both peered down the microscope doubtfully. "What do you think?" said Giles. It certainly looked peculiar but I was far from sure. Happily, an overseas doctor was working in the adjacent library and he came through at our request. "It's malaria, all right," he said. "Absolutely jumping with trophozoites. Falciparum, without a doubt." And with that he left.

Giles and I looked at each other. "What do we do now?" I asked, but by this time Giles was on the telephone to the experts on tropical disease in Liverpool. Although well past midnight, they were more than helpful. Giles called out the regimen while I wrote it down. We summoned the pharmacist from his bed and within the hour the patient was on anti-malarial therapy.

On Monday, the Chief appeared. He was horrified to see who had looked after his patients for the past forty-eight hours. "How did you get on?" he asked us cautiously. "Well," said Giles, "We thought the patients were all under control, except for that chap in the corner. We were a bit uneasy about him and sure enough, sir, he went into rigors on Saturday night. I knew, from speaking to him, that he had been in Korea, so we immediately thought of malaria. We took some blood and stained it by the modified Leishman technique and this confirmed our diagnosis. If you care to look, sir, we have set up a microscope for you. Absolutely jumping with trophozoites. Falciparum, don't you think?" Giles took a deep breath. "Well, having diagnosed malaria, sir, we put him on the Liverpool therapeutic regimen right away. His temperature has now settled and he appears much better this morning."

The Chief looked at us both for a long minute. "Gentlemen," he said at last, "I shall watch your careers with considerable interest."

"At last, just what we've always needed!" said the social anthropologist in Central Africa, gazing in delight at the title page of *The Lancet* for March 16, 1968. The item that pleased him? "A Portable Incubator for Long-distance Transport of Cultures" of course.

HEALTH-WISE, our archaeological expedition was well equipped. When we set off for a Scottish island we had with us two doctors. As one was a GP and the other a psychiatrist, body and mind were both catered for. We also had a pharmacist, a physiotherapist, and a lab technician. The GP had a varied collection of drugs ranging from aspirin to ergometrine. The pharmacist contributed numerous empty drug tins. The physiotherapist brought some nylon rope. (It came in very handy as a clothes-line.) The technician came equipped with slides and test-tubes. We hoped to use these for pollen analysis but were prepared to do a bit of parasitology if necessary. The psychiatrist didn't believe in drugs but expressed willingness to hypnotise anyone who needed an operation.

Unfortunately the party remained very healthy. The GP offered to keep himself available at surgery hours, but no-one came. The psychiatrist looked vainly for group neurosis and suggested interpretations of dreams at breakfast. When the lab technician hurt his foot he did not consult the physiotherapist; she was his wife, so doubtless he had his reasons.

Gradually our professional functions faded into the background as we all became archaeologists. Like agitated hornets we buzzed about the island on an assortment of scooters and motorbikes; and it was this mode of transport which led to the only medical emergency. After a couple of cold wet days the psychiatrist noticed puzzling red itchy areas on both hands. Medical and lay opinion was sought and the diagnosis was unanimous. In the middle of one of the best summers for years, I had chilblains.

As a mere journeyman surgeon, I am grateful to the anaesthetists who kindly allow me to operate during their anaesthetics. They are so full of charm and science that, as the end-point of a half-hour induction approaches, I am allowed to feel that I also serve by standing and waiting – a pawn in the advancement of knowledge. The most pedestrian pieces in my surgical repertoire now attain the dignity of an appendage to original pharmacological research. I am forgiven when gentle traction on a pile spoils the oscillograph recording; and if my thumb on the aorta fails to agree with the monitoring console, it is only indirectly and politely implied that my thumb should be sent for servicing and recalibration.

It was therefore with excitement, but not surprise, that I saw on entering the hospital the other day a notice which read "Meeting on Necro-anaesthesia". At last, I thought, those magnificent men with their trying machines have achieved the ultimate. I ran up to offer breathless congratulations to an anaesthetic colleague who happened to be standing near. "Surely," he said, somewhat crisply, "surely anyone could see it is a misprint for neuroanaesthesia."

Our village chemist's shop stands on a corner of the main street. It has rather small windows, a narrow entrance and a bell which jingles when the door is opened. Outside, there is a large black stone, the remains of a hitching post or a boundary marker. Inside, in a sort of ordered confusion, is a mixture of the old and the new: sophisticated toiletries and jars of a Victorian recipe hand-cream; antibiotics and simple herbs; electric razors and animal-hair shaving brushes; computerised cameras and old framed prints. It is one of the few remaining places where you can buy menthol crystals, cinnamon sticks, oil of cloves, and smelling salts. There is even a chair for the older customers.

The shop has been there a long time and the present owner, now assisted by his son, has been dispensing for over half a century. Such is his reputation that many people consult him before seeking the advice of our local group practice; and others are reluctant to accept a script until he has assured them that it will do them good.

Some of us, a privileged few, are allowed into the back premises, a rare jumble of boxes, bags, racks, and glass-fronted cabinets. Indeed, our opinion is sometimes sought as we stand drinking a cup of tea, when a customer seeks a remedy for a particular complaint. This diagnosis and treatment at a distance is by consensus judgment. Those taking part include from time to time, the pharmacist, the florist next door, a shop assistant, a policeman, a drug-company representative, and our local traffic warden. My own views are given but scant attention because I am no longer in active clinical practice. I often wonder if the patient realises the long discussion, argument, and tales of personal experience which go into the choice of an appropriate medicine. Probably not. In any case, the favoured medicaments are always the tried, trusted, and true. If they do but little good, they will certainly do no harm. From my own point of view, it is a pleasant way to spend an hour before facing the hazards of the anonymous and intimidating shelves of our old grocer's emporium, now rebuilt and refurbished as a modern supermarket.

The efforts of our little infection-control committee are beginning to bear fruit. For months we have stressed the need for meticulous observance of ward discipline. At the same time, we have taken a hard look at ward-cleaning procedures; every cubicle and side ward is now equipped with its own mop and damp dusting cloth, which remain in situ until the patient is discharged. Imagine our joy when we observed our senior surgeon washing his hands after examining each patient; this is a thing that has scarce happened before in living memory. It seems churlish to mention that he will persist in drying his wet hands on the cleaner's "J cloth".

As an ageing neurologist I retain a certain respect for the old euphemisms and eponyms of medicine, now, alas, so unfashionable, and am still pleased occasionally to hear "lues" and "luetic" instead of "syphilis" and "syphilitic". Imagine my joy when I received a summary of the notes about a patient sent to me for consultation, and read at the end of it that "The conclusions at this stage are that there is no evidence of interstitial keratitis nor of any of the other stigmata of Louise." Perhaps the myth of airborne infection in this scourge of Venus is due for revival, carried no doubt on every whispering little breeze.

My consultant friend Giles plays golf to win. Not for him the quaint philosophy of the game's the thing. When he sets out, he has only one object in mind – success. Not that he is an outstanding player. Far from it. Quite frankly, he is no more than average, but what he lacks in skill he makes up for in guile. For example, if he is playing with an older man he always calls him "sir" and offers to pull his caddy car when nearing a hill. This ensures that his partner will over-drive and lose his accuracy. Near the green he calls loudly "Watch out for that bunker!" The other's ball will make for the sand like a bullet. When a younger adversary is getting the better of him, he persistently admires his swing. After a while he asks humbly if he might stand behind and study it. "Ah," he will say, "I see what you are doing. You are keeping your elbow well in." This is guaranteed to produce a king-size slice. Approaching the green he recalls Sam Snead's description of the professional golfer's nightmare – the putting "twitches" – and offers his own opinion of a cure. Think of shoulders instead of hands, he says. This makes good green play impossible.

His real ability is the assessment of his opponent's character. Encouraging recklessness into the impossible shot; agreeing with prudence in the over-safe approach; stimulating impatience at the cost of precision; or assisting the fastidious putter to a point where he cannot do anything right. He knows it all.

He says his finest moment was in the club championship last year. He was playing against an older man whose parsimony was equalled only by his craving to win prizes. He was totally impervious to my friend's wiles. As they approached the 15th tee they were all square. Giles looked at the lake which lay alongside the fairway. "Excuse me," he said. "There is something I must do which I have wanted to do for years." So saying, he slowly unwrapped a brand new golf ball and, under the disbelieving eyes of his rival, tee-ed up and drove it into the middle of the lake. After that his antagonist could do nothing right. Giles romped home.

RETRACT, Mr Barlow. . . . Thank you. As I was telling Sister yesterday, one look at the Parthenon convinced me that the artists of ancient Greece make the architects of our great Gothic cathedrals look like pedlars in Birmingham pottery. . . . If you will kindly retract, Mr Barlow . . . and take your head out of the field of operation. Thank you so much. There is a discipline, a strength, a cleanliness of line, an economy which is quite sublime; and of course they are never brash enough to conceive of decoration without usage.

The whole building is built on Beauty. Beauty is not incidental to it or encrusted upon it . . . which is where the Italians fall into grievous sin. I wonder, Mr Barlow, if you can exert a steady, constant, and unremitting pressure on the retractor? You start well but you do not persevere; remember St John – *Qui autem perseveraverit usque in finem, hic salvus erit.* And I am sure you would wish to be saved.

Did you know that the columns which support the great entablature are several inches thicker in the middle than at the base or capital? If this small point had not been considered the columns would have looked waisted and the result, of course, disastrous. I don't think our very capable anaesthetist has yet observed that the re-breathing bag is no longer moving. Retract, Mr Barlow. Remember that I am entirely dependent on you for the success of the operation. Tell me, I am intrigued . . . why did you take up surgery so late in life?

Well Sir, I felt, Sir, that I had to save at least one human life before I died.

But why not a coastguard m'boy?

ONE'S reputation in this world hangs but by a thread. My thread was broken disastrously one Monday afternoon. After lunch I was due at a cottage hospital 16 miles away to do some radiology. As I was starting my lunch the radiographer rang up to say, with apologies, that she had (legitimately) had the morning off, and had been home for the weekend, but had missed her train connection. She had managed to get as far as the nearest junction, but could not get to the hospital until about half an hour after I was due to start screening. With a detour of barely a couple of miles, I picked her up and took her along to the cottage hospital. She had been flat-shifting, and had a huge, now empty, suitcase with her. Being, I hope, or at least pretending to be, a gentleman, I naturally thought of carrying this great thing. The hospital is a friendly place, and as we passed the theatre the sister called out "Hullo! Did you have a good . . ." and faded into silence as her jaw dropped at the sight of me walking behind, carrying what might reasonably be thought to be a weekend case. Thus was the thread of my reputation broken (or embroidered).

THE latest issue of the *Journal of the Medical Defence Union* includes a list of inquiries received by the MDU during the past twelve months which were judged to fall outside the range of matters it should handle on behalf of its members. The list referred to the following incidents and circumstances.

1. Hitting a policeman.
2. Speeding at 103 mph on a motorway.
3. Drunken driving.
4. Domestic parking dispute with neighbour.
5. Member's own divorce and custody proceedings.
6. Member's theft of 70p from a telephone box.
7. Debt collection of unpaid private fees.
8. Making own complaint regarding a relative's hospital care.
9. Planning application.
10. Income-tax assessment.
11. Domestic burglary.
12. Vandalism of car while parked in school playground.
13. Recommendation of private solicitor for non-medical problems.

As it happens, we know the chap who made the inquiries. They arose in relation to a routine professional visit to a retired schoolmaster, immobilised with arthritis, in a village seven miles along the motorway from the surgery.

Our acquaintance, at times an irascible man, had been put in a bad temper that morning by the arrival of an outrageous income-tax assessment, together with a letter from his lawyer about his impending divorce. He decided to call at the lawyer's office on his way to see the patient, and to take with him his copy of planning proposals for a new lavatory complex for the use of his patients, over which a dispute had arisen. His mood did not improve when he found that his study had been broken into during the night, and that his portable typewriter and his home computer had been taken; the desk had been ransacked, and the plans were nowhere to be seen.

After finishing the afternoon surgery he left on his mission, only to find his car boxed in, not for the first time, by the intrusive parking of his next-door neighbour. After some pretty violent backing and filling, which dented both cars, he drove in a fury to the lawyer's office, where he rapidly formed the opinion that the firm was quite incapable of understanding the iniquity of his wife, who was claiming custody of his only son, and wholly unfit to cope with the criminal negligence of the agency he employed to collect bad debts from his private patients. It would be madness to entrust them with the legal side of the lavatory plans, and as he drove along the motorway he resolved to consult a new firm for all his future problems.

When he arrived at his patient's house it was to find that he had been taken away two days ago to live with his daughter; nobody knew where they had gone. Our acquaintance went to the nearest telephone box to ring his secretary in case she might know the daughter's address, but the phone was out of order. As he left the box he noticed a small pile of money, 70p in all, left on the shelf by a previous frustrated caller. Conscience is the still small voice which warns us that somebody may be watching, and he took a good look round before pocketing the money – as seemed his due in the circumstances.

Outside, he had a better idea, and drove to the village school, where his patient had taught, to ask if they could help. School had finished for the day, but one or two boys were kicking a football round as he parked the car in the playground. The headmaster was delighted to see him, and invited him to take a wee dram in his study. It transpired that the daughter's address was not a quarter of a mile from our acquaintance's surgery, and so overcome was he on hearing this that a further dram became necessary. This led him to ventilate his wrongs to a sympathetic audience, and eventually he recollected yet a further grievance, and discoursed with feeling on the atrocious indignities suffered by his cousin, a patient in the local cottage hospital, where the headmaster served as a member of the board.

By the time he left it was several drinks later, and in the interim one of his tyres had been slashed and one of his headlights kicked in by the young gentlemen who had been playing football. The faint haze which had formed in front of his eyes turned to a sombre red, and somewhat unsteadily and with gritted teeth he changed the wheel.

It was getting dark as he drove back on the motorway, taking his rage out on the accelerator pedal. Unfortunately the police had a speed trap in operation, and he was tracked at 103 mph and stopped. As he now smelled strongly of alcohol, the officiating policeman produced a breathalyser. This was the last straw. Our acquaintance surged from the car and struck the policeman a powerful blow on the stomach.

Next day, out on bail on charges of speeding, drunken driving, resisting arrest, and assaulting the police in the performance of their duties, he spent several hours framing a letter to the Medical Defence Union; it was quite late when he had recovered sufficiently to visit his patient.

IT is generally agreed by anaesthetists that a calendar is more useful than a clock in neurosurgical operating-theatres. I was reminded of this the other day when a patient actually was twice as old at the end of operation as he had been at the beginning. Perhaps in fairness to my neurosurgical colleague I should add that the operation was on a 2½-hour-old baby.

PATHOLOGIST, seeking improvements to his department, at staff committee: "We must think of our public image. Of course the mortuary is the shop window of a hospital."

THE punctuality, or otherwise, of consultants is a major factor in the efficiency (or otherwise) of any appointment system for outpatients. My 26-mile journey to a neighbouring city does not present any problems when the weather is good. When the weather is bad, however, the road can be a brute, and it is sometimes impassable. In winter, until the train services were cut so much that a return to my base hospital on the same day became almost impossible, I used the train regularly. It meant that I arrived some 30 minutes later in the morning, after a three-quarter-mile trudge in wellingtons through snow and slush. I used to warn the hospital in advance, asking that the first appointments be delayed by 30 minutes. Some weeks later I asked if this had been done, and was told that it had not been necessary. The patients were told on arrival that the specialist liked his patients to sit quietly for 30 minutes before he examined them.

WHEN I was a student, our senior surgeon, Sir A B-C, was an absentee clinician and his outpatient clinic was always done by his registrar, Mr Eager. One day Sir A, having nothing better to do, thought it would be a pleasant change to attend the hospital. After a rapturous welcome from Sister, he sat down at his place in outpatients and Mr Eager was banished to a cubicle. The first patient appeared, and looked most disconcerted. "What's the trouble, my man?" "I always see Sir A B-C," replied the patient (obviously a chronic). The great man rose, took the man over to Mr Eager in his corner, and said, "Sir A, your patient."

I DROPPED into our chemist's shop the other day and there found a colleague from the town over the hill. He was paying cash for kaolin and neomycin. The chemist was puzzled and genuinely distressed. "If only you would get an NHS prescription, Doctor, you would not have to pay me all this money."

A few minutes later I found him stowing the stuff in the boot of his car. I asked him what he was doing. He looked round cautiously. "The children have D&V again. I expect they have picked it up at school." "Then why not get your GP in, Sandy." "We have had this trouble before. Our GP is an awfully keen lad, I think very highly of him. The trouble is that he keeps sending specimens to the lab. Last time it was 6 weeks before they cleared the kids with three consecutive negative specimens each. For 5½ of those weeks we had three perfectly healthy, boisterous children confined in our small house by a combination of quarantine and bad weather. In the end my wife was on tranquillisers. This time she insists that I deal with it myself."

SURELY great possibilities are opened up in the NHS by the surgeon at our hospital who wrote: "This patient requires a hernia for his truss."

"You took your time," said Giles. "Well," I replied. "I had to convince them you were not a case needing compulsory admission. And, believe me, that was not easy considering the way you were carrying on. Besides, these mental hospitals are not easy to find."

"It was all so humiliating," said Giles, as we drove home. "Simply humiliating. And all because I tried to help a poor unfortunate soul. If I ever meet him again, so help me, I will do him an injury." In hurt tones he told me his story. Apparently he had an elderly professional man in one of his side-rooms suffering from episodic delusions, the result of a lifetime's dedication to his favourite tipple. After a lot of heart-searching Giles decided he must be transferred to one of our local psychiatric units for the appropriate care and treatment. The patient was far from happy and protested vigorously. In the course of an increasingly heated conversation, he referred to my friend as a "white-coated fascist". Giles had a splendid idea. He took off his coat so that they could talk to each other, man to man, in their ordinary clothes. There could then be no trappings of authority. This had little effect. In fact, his patient's agitation increased and, with it, returned the familiar apparitions. Vampire bats and snarling wolves, to be precise. Giles knew the escorts were due to arrive at any minute so he thought to humour the man. "The bats are not so bad," he said, soothingly, picking up an empty bedpan. "Just hit them with something like this." "What about the wolves?" asked his patient. "Simple," said Giles, standing on a chair. "Keep out of their reach and kick them off."

At that point, three large male nurses from the asylum entered the room. Giles, carried away with his demonstration, was now upon the ward table swatting invisible bats with a bedpan, whilst kicking away imaginary wolves with his feet. Quick as a flash, the erstwhile detainee slipped on Giles' white coat and put Giles' stethoscope round his neck. "A very bad case," he said to the attendants as he walked slowly from the ward, shaking his head sadly.

HE was an experienced and skilful surgeon but absent minded, es-pecially when flustered. One day he was to perform a very minor operation which among certain races constitutes a religious rite. Arriving late for the appointment, he was met by the mother holding the victim in her arms. Patting the infant on the head, he said "What a delightful baby!", and then with his best smile, "Is it a boy or a girl?"

WHY did I ask for this laboratory investigation? Now that I have the result in my hand, I have no idea why I ordered it. It has, as far as I can see, no possible bearing on the case. Whatever the result, it would not influence the diagnosis or the treatment. In any case, I do not know the normal values and therefore do not know whether the results are abnormal. My book is too out of date to mention it.

Why did I ask for it? Could it be that I read an article about it? I have no recollection of doing so. Perhaps some of my friends suggested it, but I can't think how or why. Was it perhaps some new idea that flitted in and out of my brain? I had better ring up the pathologist and ask him about it. No, this test has occupied several man-hours in the lab. It might cause ill-feeling if I now ask what is its significance. In fact, I had better keep out of the way of all pathologists for the next few days in case *they* ask *me* about it.

Perhaps I ought to go to the library to find out about it. Quite apart from pathologists, the Chief may ask me why I ordered it. Yet even if I read the latest literature on the subject I still won't know why I ordered it for this patient. It would really be simpler to send the whole thing for filing before the Chief sees it at all. Wait a minute, I remember now. The Chief ordered it himself. That at least lets me out. But why did he order it? I'm sure he doesn't know. He will have no recollection of it now and won't know the normal values any more than I do. Furthermore, he will expect me to explain it to him and whatever I say will put him in a bad mood.

Yes, the wisest course is to send it for filing before he sees it. He won't remember it, the pathologists won't tackle him about it, and we will continue to treat the patient in the usual manner, as we would have done in any case.

THREE medical men – a surgeon, a physician, and a psychiatrist – were having a discussion with a sector manager when someone asked them what 2 plus 2 makes. The surgeon, without hesitation, said 5, and looked round, defying anyone to contradict him. The physician, rather apologetically, said he would not like to commit himself until he had done some tests and had the results to hand, but if forced to give an off-the-cuff opinion, he thought that, perhaps, the answer would turn out to be somewhere in between 3 and 6. The sector manager replied that, at this moment in time, he could not give a definite answer to the question posed, and that he would need to obtain clearance from the district general manager before attempting an answer, but, without in any way committing himself, he felt that, at the end of the day, it would not be found that the answer was any less than it might previously have been predicted. The psychiatrist just sat silent with his fingertips together for a couple of minutes looking at the questioner; then, leaning forward, he asked, "Why do you want to know? Why is it so important to you what 2 plus 2 makes?"

THOSE who know Ambrose Bierce's *The Devil's Dictionary* will detect the inspiration for the following definitions. This recipe is to be taken slowly, with a little water. Add salt to taste.

*Surgeon.* – A practitioner who acts first and then thinks.

*Physician.* – A practitioner who thinks first and defers action.

*Anaesthetist.* – A practitioner who makes a surgeon think.

*Community physician.* – A practitioner who seldom thinks of a single patient.

*Radiologist.* – A practitioner who thinks he sees things.

*Psychiatrist.* – A practitioner who thinks thinking is the thing.

*Paediatrician.* – A practitioner who thinks he is an adult.

*Medical journalist.* – A practitioner who thinks he knows what other practitioners think.

OUR recent winter, the thought of which still makes me shiver, caused me to consider how doctors and plumbers are really brothers under the skin. Both are neglected by most of the people most of the time – but, when needed, they have to come running. Like the doctor in an emergency (and what to do with plumbing is not?), the plumber's services must be immediately to hand. No excuse is acceptable: he is on his rounds; he is attending another case; there is a queue of people in the shop; he is asleep with exhaustion. Not good enough! He is needed at once. And no, leaving a message with the receptionist will not do. It is of the utmost urgency.

I was reminded again of the affinity when our own plumber called recently. The speculative look at the drip from the ceiling. The more detailed examination with torch and special tools. The sad shaking of the head. Why, he asked, had he not been called in sooner. I thought it would go away I heard myself say. Then the jargon. It is only a malfunctioning grommet, he says, in the rotor arm of the ballcock outflow valve. Is it serious, I ask, my voice cracking with emotion? His countenance took on an even graver look. I knew it! Major surgery. A new bathroom suite. How will the family live through it? The need for a second opinion flashes through my mind. After all, he is only a general plumber. What I need is a specialist in outflow valves. I clear my throat and screw up courage to make the request. But, almost like a mind reader, his face clears. Not to worry, he says, he can make it better. What joy! What relief! I gaze on him with affection. However, he says, could I assist him by collecting an item from the local hardware store. I wait patiently while he writes something on a pad in his illegible handwriting. The grommet cost me £1.30, which at that time was the same as the prescription charge in the NHS.

DISCONTENTED with the retrospective omniscience of the morbid anat-omists, the physicians decided to invite them to attend formal ward rounds to ascertain whether they were as perspicacious while the patients were still wrapped in their skins and (more or less) alive.

Whether it was really successful as an intellectual exercise I do not know, but I understand it led to much merry repartee of a rather arcane nature – "Well, Mr Bloggs, this is Dr Snookes, another specialist, and he will soon be able to give us a definite opinion on your problem, eh Dr Snookes?" This invariably produced beams of delight from Mr Bloggs, as blissfully unaware of the reasons for the grins on all the medical faces as a Smithfield champion eyed by butchers.

Of course there was intense speculation among the patients as to who Dr Snookes might be. Ward sisters knew, but weren't telling; junior nurses might have told but did not know, so all was well until the physicians admitted a girl whose mother worked as a cleaner in the pathology department offices. Hearing about the Great Mystery during the course of a general discussion one visiting time, mother was able to enlighten the ward that Dr Snookes and his colleagues were "the ones what cuts people up to find out what they went and died of". This piece of information broke all records for travelling the whole length of the hospital grapevine.

I do not think that either physicians or pathologists appreciated why the patients made such a fuss, nor did they take kindly to a managerial order to cease the practice. However, cease it they did. Mind, some of us, looking on from the sidelines, wondered if the information was not an inspired leak, deliberately organised by the pathologists, who were, it seems, proving no better than the physicians at ante-mortem diagnosis.

ONE of our senior anaesthetists retired recently. He was much respected and regarded as a tower of strength by his colleagues. It is difficult to imagine how the void created by his departure will ever be filled. Who else could produce this remark to a surgeon, during a bloody upper abdominal operation: "I've just opened another bottle of blood. Shall I give it to the patient or just pour it straight into the sucker?"

New students are still told the story of how the good doctor, when passing an open doorway, saw a surgeon doing a rectoscopy. Seeing his chance – he was not on good terms with the surgeon – he put his head round the doorway and shouted "Cough!" The patient obeyed, and the surgeon, showered, drew back in amazement. "What on earth do you think you're playing at?" he gasped. "Sorry," came the reply. "I thought he looked a bit blue."

SOME nights ago, towards two o'clock, I was roused from a healing sleep by a confused blundering and muttering sound from downstairs. This turned out to be a friend (another of us alienated bachelors) who, having dined liberally, found to his concern on the way home that the road would not stay firmly in front of his car and so prudently sought the nearest place of refuge. All he could say at the time was "Well, you shouldn't leave your front door open when you're out." He was duly lashed down in the spare bed till morning.

The following weekend it was my turn for hospital duty and when I returned to the cottage at dusk on the Monday, I was rather slow to realise that I couldn't get in. All doors and windows were firmly shut and impossible to open; this puzzled me rather because, unless I'm in the grip of serious preoccupations, I never lock the doors (consequently, I never carry the keys) and always leave a window open as part of the cat's domestic arrangements. A trip across the village to my landlord did not produce any suitable spare keys so there was nothing for it but to burgle the joint. My amiable GP neighbour produced some black treacle and brown paper and the village handyman-cum-glazier agreed to come round and help as soon as he'd finished his supper.

While waiting for my burglar's mate to arrive I quite enjoyed spreading the treacle on the paper; he came in time to pass the resulting product up to me on the kitchen lean-to roof. A moment later, the window was a crumpled and treacly mass, lying in the bath and I was inside. A quick glance showed me that the cat had somehow got in and eaten his weekend's food supply – a fresh mystery. Perturbed, I went on downstairs and there on the doormat lay a packet, wrapped in brown paper but not bearing postage stamps. Delivered by hand, of course; so that was why the door-latch was down for the first time in years. Inside the package – a peace offering – were some choice panatellas, a limerick with a distinctly Oedipal twist, and a note of renewed thanks for the hospitality of a few nights before, ending with an apologetic reminder that people who leave their doors unlocked must expect trouble.

Septimus Thaddeus O'Mach. Now there's a name to conjure with. I doubt, nay am certain, that those among you who make so glib with the organ of Zuckerkandl, the ligament of Wrisberg, or the membrane of Reissner will never have heard of that great Irishman, Septimus Thaddeus O'Mach, anatomist and surgeon extraordinary to Napoleon Bonaparte.

O'Mach's great treatise on gastrointestinal anatomy led to the general use of the term "The gastric organ of Septimus Thaddeus O'Mach". However, O'Mach's contemporaries got fed up with such a mouthful, and it soon was digested down to "the organ of S. T. O'Mach", and finally just plain "Stomach". Napoleon put the final imprimatur on the name at the famous interview with Maréchal Ney. Ney had been complaining about the cost of the army's boot repairs on the way back from Moscow.

Napoleon was just about to utter a lifeless platitude about an army marching on its feet when he was interrupted in mid-sentence by the arrival of O'Mach. Thus it came out: "An army marches on its . . . S. T. O'Mach!" If you don't believe it, try it in French with a Corsican accent: "Une armée marche sur ces . . . S. T. O'Mach!"

Napoleon's publicity men were on hand and the great man's witty saying flashed around the world. Within no time at all they were giggling over it in Boston just as Napoleon was landing in St Helena.

To those of us whose studies of physiology are still so clear in our minds that we cannot pass a frog's leg without twitching, the above comments will doubtless chase up the memories of Tom, the man with a gastric fistula. Tom, as you will recall, had been shot in the stomach by a grizzly bear in the course of some nasty little incident which need not detain us further. However, be that as it may, Tom had become particularly sensitive about his relations with the larger carnivora so that when a certain well-known physiologist was peering at his gastric mucosa, what should happen but that same man be addressed as "Dr Wolf" by a colleague. Tom blenched, beads of sweat stood out on his brow, and beads of acid on his reddened stomach lining – Can you wonder that he had the STOMache?

THE sudden snap of wintry weather made me put on my new suit. My others have grown small for me, but this new suit (of unusual colour and design) gives plenty of room for those extra articles of clothing which make all the difference between starvation and comfort on a cold day.

At breakfast my family approved the suit. At the office our head typist said, "Clothes do make such a difference." The caretaker said I was "perjink". The health visitor thought that the line was lovely and the pattern not in the least loud. Others took it in at a silent glance. I paid no attention to a remark by the health inspector about Joseph's coat, as I am sure it had nothing to do with me.

I have always given names to my suits. There was my Final-year Suit, my Qualifying Suit, my Darlington Memorial Suit (bought in my first house-job): then my Marriage Suit, and my Demob Suit. I still have two Anaesthetic Suits (the ones that have grown small) bought with the fees from dental anaesthetics. My present Sunday suit is known as my Polio Jags Suit, as I was able to buy it after doing extra inoculation sessions for another authority. When I met my chief he eyed my new rig-out and said, "Oh Boy, what a suit!" I told him about my suit-naming custom, and he at once christened this one my Tycoon Suit. "It was the only one in the shop that fitted me," I said defensively, "44 Portly, is how the assistant there described it."

POINT the forceps up a little, Barlow. Thank you *so* much. Cut. Shorter! A little shorter, Barlow; don't be afraid. I am very good-tempered. About ⅛ inch. Ah! I see our ideas of absolute measurement are quite, quite different. Cut the gut just sufficiently far away to keep the knot happy.

Now I know what you mean, Sir.

Good! I felt confident that in time I would find a formula which would appeal to you. And now if you will, just for a moment, take your head out of the field of operation . . . Thank you. Some day, Barlow, and quite by accident of course, I shall scalp you. Nurse, wipe Mr Barlow's brow. We have no evidence to show his sweat is sterile . . . Now there's an idea for your MD thesis – *The Flora on the Surgeon's Brow* – rather like the opening bar of a Sitwell poem

> The Flora on the Surgeon's Brow
> Oleum, Olei, Olea, Oleow.

I once wrote a poem in my student days . . . a rather sad little piece. I think I can recall the first line . . . "Why, Oh why, did the wicked Hormone?" which is prettily scanned, don't you agree?

Indeed, Sir.

If you lean very heavily on the patient's chest, Barlow, he stops breathing. Have you noticed?

Sorry, Sir!

Cut. Shorter! No, not off. Just shorter. Again. Cut . . . it's really quite extraordinary . . . once you get a pair of scissors in your hand, Barlow, you change from a very decent quiet young man into a thyrotoxic barber. Relax m'boy. Hold your breath and count five hundred . . . very slowly.

Yes, Sir. Sorry, Sir.

Don't apologise. An apology establishes guilt which will, in time, give you a complex of inadequacy. When are you going on holiday, Barlow?

On the 24th, Sir.

I shall miss you m'boy. We shall all miss Mr Barlow, won't we sister?

ONE of our housemen is wearing a permanent grin; but the more sensitive ward sister still shudders at the thought. Last week on the senior physician's round, the dear old lady in bed 6 announced loudly to a recent arrival that the old gentleman was one of these out-of-date doctors who was taking a refreshment course. The clever young house doctor, she added, kindly took him round to see the interesting cases once a week.

THIS week at our hospital the builders are working, with all their paraphernalia down to pneumatic drills, directly over the theatre. This has somewhat confused the Thoracic Surgeon, whose decibel output as he split a sternum almost equalled theirs. But the builders got in first. They sent down a message asking if he could make less noise.

Dr Algernon Fitzherbert-MacWilliams, the eminent psychiatrist, took the stand, the oath, and the expectant audience in one all-embracing piercing glance. "Tealeaf is not suffering from any psychiatric disorder," he said.

There was a sudden silence in the Crown Court, in the case of R v Harry Tealeaf, and the judge stiffened as he prepared to listen to the sentences from the witness before pronouncing his own one sentence.

"Harry", continued the witness "is a normal villain who preys on honest citizens because he likes his way of life and has done very well out of it. He has no obsessions, phobias, or anxiety neurosis, nor does he exhibit any depression, delusions, or even illusions. His compulsion to acquire things is no different from that of everybody else, except in his way of achieving his objective, at which he is extremely proficient.

"His falling out of his pram when eight months of age is entirely irrelevant, although his recovery turned out to be unfortunate . . . for others. What he saw or heard in the woodshed when three years of age was merely an example of healthy sexuality which gave him an appetite to acquire the wealth, when older, to gratify such urges. At puberty, his masturbation caused no perturbation, but added to his urges to be a master . . . at acquiring property, as a reality and not as a psychological symbol. He stole the items on the present charge-sheet simply because he wanted them and knew their beauty and value.

"My lord, I do speak here as an expert witness, for who knows the beauty and value of the stolen articles better than myself? It was *my* house which he broke into. All the treasures were mine, having been slowly amassed over the years by diligence and charging high fees when coming to Court to assist in psychiatric defence of criminals."

*Moral: Booty is in the eye of the beholder.*

PERIPATETICS were so called because, like Aristotle, they walked about while lecturing: perhaps that is why their logic loses its grip when they attempt the Archimedean method of philosophising in the bath. Surgeons are *not* chaps who know that if they can't cut it out, it isn't there. They may be chaps who know that if they can't see it and feel it, it is psychological; and if they can't cut it out, it is incurable.

Giles' interest in the law dates back to a startling performance in the medical jurisprudence viva exam. His reply to blood coagulation was based upon a story by Dorothy L. Sayers; his exposition on rigor mortis came from R. Austin Freeman; and his distinction-winning answer concerning belladonna poisoning was lifted directly from Agatha Christie. He was just getting into his stride regarding the role of the expert witness, from Cecil Roberts, when the examiner called a halt. I think they had both been reading the same books.

His most dramatic moment was when he appeared as a defence witness for his hospital authority. As a young casualty officer he had set a Colles fracture to the best of his ability. The procedure lacked both an anaesthetic and evidence of gratitude, for the patient sued. Giles, as they say, burned the midnight oil at both ends studying this particular fracture: its causes, variations, treatment, and complications. There was no question, he asserted, which if asked he could not answer. On the day, the plaintiff's barrister rose slowly to his feet and he asked but one question. "Doctor," he inquired. "How long were you qualified when you treated this unfortunate man?" "Two months," replied Giles. "No further questions, m'lud" said learned counsel sitting down. The matter was settled out of court.

# III

# Students and Professors

HE was awarded full-column obituaries: deservedly, because he was a great healer, an unparalleled teacher, and a man of good humour and humility. I knew him best as a teacher some fifty years ago. Like most of us in those days, he was impecunious. To keep the wolf at bay, he coached backward students, which included Francis Flute and me, for our finals. By this means he just managed to hire a room in Harley Street for one afternoon a week. The pittance Francis and I could afford to pay was so ludicrously inadequate that we sought means by which we could repay his kindness; and what better method than by dressing his waiting-room? This we proceeded to do, despite his protests.

Francis and I took the different roles turn and turn about. When I was No 1 I would install myself in the waiting-room some minutes before the Real Patient was due. Enter Real Patient. I would smile and nod and pass the time of day, and remark that our doctor had been delayed, adding reassuringly that my own case would not take long. Then Francis, No 2, would enter, remarking to all and sundry that he was miles too early. We would then recognise each other as nodding acquaintances who had met some time before in that very waiting-room. Both of us were members of the Hospital Dramatic Society, and it was splendid practice for us; we just played it by ear. I might divulge that Sir Edward had recommended me to consult this doctor. Francis, in rejoinder, would have been directed to him by his GP, who "thought the world of him". Sometimes the Real Patient would join in, and that made it all the more fun.

The receptionist would enter and ask, "Mr Peter Quince?", and I would rise and follow. In less than no time I emerged, smiling and ostentatiously tucking my chequebook away. Bidding the company good luck and farewell, I departed. The Real Patient would then be summoned and Francis would settle down to his crossword or his pocket *Aids to Medicine*. Even after the Real Consultation was over he had to hang about for a good quarter-of-an-hour to give the Real Patient time to get clear of the neighbourhood. (Once they had nearly collided at Baker Street station.)

We kept our ploy as secret as possible, but it wasn't long before we learned that a "rival" further down the Street had seized the same idea. This we decided we must investigate; we might perhaps learn something to improve our own technique. Accordingly, Francis turned up bearing a small parcel and sat until the receptionist next appeared, when he handed it over, saying, "From the Hospital. Urgent", and then departed. At teatime he reported to me: "That man is using his *family* – his sisters and his cousins and his aunts. They all stopped talking when I entered and stared at me like a lot of cows in a field. I was obviously unexpected. They were struck dumb. No finesse, no style. I just handed over my package and bolted. Don't you think, Peter, we might offer to coach them?" "No, Francis," I replied, "they could never afford our fees. By the way, what was in that parcel of yours?" "Just a brace of kippers," he said. "Do for their tea."

NOBODY quite understood how Robinson passed his exams since he appeared averse to any form of studying. Even as a clinical student he was rarely seen in the wards and never at a lecture. It was not long before we found ourselves doing midwifery and there was considerable speculation on Robinson's debut. The very first evening Robinson was called out he turned down all offers of help and we waited expectantly for the phone to ring. It was not long, however, before Robinson returned smiling quietly and assuring us that all had gone off perfectly and he had delivered a fine son and heir. He also added that he could not see why so much fuss was made over what was, after all, a perfectly natural process.

There was a slight sense of anticlimax and little interest was shown when Robinson was called a second time. The telephone call came, I remember, during a game of poker. "It's Robinson," someone called. "He sounds worried and is asking for help." I hurried to the telephone. "Hullo, what's the trouble?" I asked and could not help adding, "I thought childbirth was a perfectly natural process." "Natural!" Robinson almost exploded down the telephone. "Natural childbirth is all right, but this one is coming out head first."

THE candidate was doing well. He had dropped no marks on any of the oral questions. He was, in fact, doing a little too well; both he and the examiner knew it.

"Tell me, then," the examiner asked finally, without a glimmer of a smile on his face: "What is the dose of strabismus?"

The candidate was shrewd. He stroked his chin pensively as if searching for the answer. "The – er – tincture or the solution, Sir?" he inquired. This was a good parry to the examiner's thrust.

"Well?" the examiner frowned. Things had taken a different turn from the I'm-afraid-I-don't-know-sir attitude. "The tincture of course, my boy!" It was important that he kept his flag flying at all costs. But alas, the examiner was baited with his own bait.

"Oh!" the candidate feigned surprise. "I didn't know that strabismus was soluble in alcohol!"

MY examiner sat back in his chair and, grasping his lapel firmly with one hand, said:

"I have a headache, Doctor."

I was nonplussed. This was different from the "How-do-you-treat-so-and-so" approach.

"Well – er, Sir, how long have you had it?"

"Thirty years!"

"When does it come on, Sir?"

"In the morning and wears off during the day."

So far so good. But I had ten minutes to fill, so I played for time by asking further questions.

"Anything else trouble you, Sir?"

"Yes, I'm sick in the mornings."

Silence. My mind became blank.

"Come on, lad, have you drawn no conclusions?"

"Well, Sir, the history is too long for a cerebral tumour and – er – meningitis."

I looked at him hopefully; he was playing with his spectacles – a clue.

"Eye strain, Sir?"

"Could be. Anything else?"

At this moment the bell rang. Time up. There was a scraping of chairs as candidates rose to go. What else? What else? I racked my brain. All this time he looked at me with a rather devilish smile on his face. I took a chance and crossed my fingers. I couldn't think of anything else.

"Well, Sir, it could be – er – chronic alcoholism?"

I don't know if my diagnosis was correct, but at any rate I passed.

IN a recent examination, candidates were informed that 50 of 200 guests at a wedding reception fell ill with acute diarrhoea and vomiting 2½ hours after eating the meal. The candidates were asked to comment on this event, and to advise the hotel manager on how to prevent a repetition. Two particularly perceptive answers were received:

(1) If only 50 of the 200 guests complained, the remaining 150 may have been too drunk to realise that they could blame the food eaten.

(2) The manager should apologise to the guests, avoid weddings in future, and fire the kitchen staph.

EMOTIONS tend to run high during that tense period before the onset of the examinations for higher qualifications. An unexpected sound has been known to send a coffee cup crashing to the ground and even such a simple physiological act as a sneeze has played havoc with a cohort of blood-pressures. Someone fiddling with a stethoscope or reading aloud from a medical journal can easily turn a face puce with suppressed rage. It is rare, however, for the tension to erupt into physical violence. Recently I chanced upon two surgical registrars struggling wildly on the floor. "Admit it!" yelled the upper one, holding his adversary by the shoulders and shaking him furiously. "The internal pudendal artery is lateral to the pudendal nerve." And from the taut lips of his opponent came the single word "medial!" All things considered, I am glad examinations are behind me now.

INVENTING wrong answers for multiple-choice questions conjures twisted possibilities out of my imagination. What does it conjure out of a neuroanatomist's? Perhaps something like these. The Pyramidal Tract is the principal motorway of Egypt. The superior and lateral relations of the Dentate Nucleus are with the enamel. Inferior Olive is a Greek term of personal abuse. Corpus Striatum is the official name for the African zebra. Globus Pallidus is the term for the pale eyeball of anaemia. Corpus Callosum is Latin for a manual worker. The Olfactory Bulb is Milton's phrase for the onion ("Still as they hungered, with a brimming tear The olfact'ry bulb they chew . . ." – *Paradise Lost*, Book XIII).

THE professor was walking from the infirmary to the university with the chest piece of his stethoscope dangling from his hip pocket when he was stopped by a respectful boy scout. "Excuse me Sir, but your catheter is hanging out."

THE other day when we met a friend emerging from an unfamiliar university building we were at pains to draw him out. It appeared that he had accepted the offer of the department of agriculture to put him up temporarily while repairs were being carried out in his own department. Our friend is a shy man, and stands somewhat in awe of his adopted professor, in whom many years of agriculture have matured an already hearty personality. Initially, therefore, our friend viewed his translation with some misgiving, and he was comfortably reassured to observe, standing in the entrance hall of the department, a fine brindled cow entirely composed of some plastic material, and bearing on its face an expression of disinterested benevolence.

Beyond nodding to the animal as he passed, our friend made no effort to ripen the acquaintance. One afternoon, however, as he conversed uneasily with his formidable host, a glint of sunlight revealed that the rear end of the cow, including the tail, was detachable. Our friend's knowledge of cows is undeniably sketchy, and it came to him that his horizon would be considerably enlarged could he but investigate what lay within. The next day he was at pains to choose a time when nobody was about. The catch was a little stiff, and our friend was injudicious enough to give it a smart tug. With a resounding clatter the cow overbalanced, retaining its benevolent expression but scattering plastic viscera in all directions. On all sides doors opened inquiringly, and our friend found himself surrounded by a crowd of interested and helpful agriculturalists.

Nothing was ever *said*, our friend tells us, but the cow has now been moved to the professor's room.

AN East European speaker at the conference was reading his paper in English and obviously having difficulty with the language. Halfway through the lecture, a female delegate leapt to her feet in extreme agitation and, pointing her finger at him, screamed at the top of her voice, "There's a spider on your collar and it's climbing into your hair!" Immediately the chairman and his deputy rushed forward and slapped away at his head. Shaken, but determined, the speaker finished his talk. Because of the diversion, no doubt, he received a storm of cheers and applause. Later I asked one of his countrymen if he had recovered from his somewhat unnerving experience. "I tried to explain," said his friend, "but I had to stop. He believes that his ideas were so controversial that a woman in the audience screamed at him and the chairman and his deputy attacked him physically, but by sheer force of logic he convinced the assembly of the rightness of his views and, as a result, received a standing ovation. How can I tell him it was a spider?"

As a young doctor I helped to arrange a lecture-demonstration. The event went extremely well and our guest of honour, a London professor, was obviously impressed. My chief was well pleased. After the discussion had ended and the vote of thanks given, I saw him looking round the assembly with an anxious eye. It finally came to rest on me. His face lit up and he summoned me forward. I approached, expecting a modicum of praise for the hours of work I had put into the project. True he introduced me to his distinguished guest but followed with the request: "Perhaps you would be good enough to show the professor to the nearest toilet."

OUR professor of psychology is of Presbyterian origin and legitimately prides himself on his social integrity. When he went to the university bookshop – which does sell scientific journals – to ask for a copy of *Nature*, the lady assistant's face expressed plain horror. "No, Sir," she said, "we certainly do not stock *that* type of production." The professor got the message but was lost for words and retreated in disorder.

KNOWN to the police: that was the outcome of a third-degree grilling one evening last week. A Panda car pulled up at our gate, and an unfamiliar police officer asked if I could help with some inquiries. Was it true that I was a manager of some sort of licensed club in an adjoining county? I admitted the fact.

The licence was due for renewal, and the bona fides of the managers had to be checked. Did we serve only beer, or spiritous liquors as well? I cheerfully confessed to hard liquor. And was it true that we often ran a strip performance on the premises? According to information received by the police, scantily dressed or nude female persons, and sometimes even naked males, were displayed on the stage to the gaze of our members, and strange practices were suspected of going on behind the chintz screens in the corner. Was it true that assignations for such procurement were made in advance through the postal service, and did the parties by common consent arrange to meet again? Yes, I had to admit that such was the truth and nothing but the truth.

Was it a fact that some of our meetings were attended by both male and female club members sitting close together in darkened rooms, enlivened by the projection of colour slides of parts of the human body not normally revealed to view? That we also maintained a whole library of indelicate pictures and rousing accounts of unconventional human behaviour? And that such alleged orgies were held in the lunch-hour as well as in the evenings? Apart from protesting at the orgiastic label in this permissive era, I had to admit that the facts were substantially correct. But worse was yet to come.

Was it true that cocaine derivatives were used on the club premises? And that we harboured members of an active drug chain for pushing pep pills, tranquillisers, and the hard stuff for mainliners? Yes, I had to confess that users were put in touch with the sources of supply. It was almost an anticlimax to admit that we also maintained two charming hostesses for our own permanent comfort and joy; and that young nurses from a nearby hostel were invited in from time to time. I thought that the word orgy was written in capital letters in the policeman's note-book.

You have been warned what may happen if you, too, accept an invitation to serve on the management committee of your local Postgraduate Medical Centre.

In the summer vacation the library was almost empty; the young men around bent quietly over their reading. I was a century away in the fields of East Anglia with a Victorian report on organised agricultural gangs, and my eye was caught by the following lines:

"Mixed gangs are also objected to on the grounds of indecency. In the case of females, their dress as it is often worn or arranged to avoid the wet, and the stooping nature of the work are said to involve a certain amount of exposure, which excites the notice of the other sex, and leads to indecent remarks."

A young librarian in a miniskirt walked past. Mine was the only head that turned.

The two eminent men sunning themselves by the water's edge were engaged in amiable conversation.

"Don't see you here often," mused Mr X. "Fugitive from the grindstone, I suppose, same as me. (Professor Y nodded pleasantly.) Funny thing my running into you again like this. Haven't seen you since the Smiths' party last November. That was quite a party, wasn't it? (Professor Y mentally removed all the Smiths of his acquaintance from the neat little compartments of his mind, but was unable to decide which were the guilty ones, so he nodded again as a safety measure.) Must be telepathic or something. Wife and I were only talking about you this morning, remembering all your kindness when she had that breakdown back in the spring. (The professor sighed inwardly, trying not to show his boredom.) Never cease to be grateful to you. When I think of all the worry and expense we've had in the past, and you and your firm were the only people clever enough to spot the trouble and cure it. (That word 'firm' was all too familiar. Surely, he wasn't a colleague from the infirmary – clothes didn't make that much difference to a man. A GP perhaps.) Of course, that was an inspired move of yours, taking her in those few days for observation and tests and a thorough overhaul." (Confound the fellow, why didn't he say point-blank who he was. The professor smiled his well-revered bedside smile, and ambled away.)

Mr X watched him with a puzzled frown, and said to the man on the other side of him, "Can't for the life of me remember that chap's name, but whoever he is, he's an absolute wizard with vintage cars."

I WAS late for class. Rounding a corner between two corridors, a pile of books in my hand, I slipped. My weight fell on my left hand and the next morning I had a painful swollen finger. I reported to the school doctor after breakfast. "Go to Father Oswald and get an X-ray," I was told – a simple instruction, but demanding courage in its execution. Father Oswald taught physics; he had an intimidating reputation, and to disturb him with a trifling injury was daunting.

There was, however, no need to tremble. Father Oswald was delighted. He led me and the whole class to the room where his X-ray machine was housed. It was a remarkable sight. The active parts were completely exposed, and after the blinds were drawn it sparked and glowed mysteriously. Father Oswald explained its workings in obscure jargon. My hand was placed over it and a piece of canvas like a faded oil painting was put on top. The outline of my finger bones could then be dimly perceived. One by one, the physics class leant over to look.

That was in October, 1943. Later, I suffered more serious injuries, when Father Oswald's radiography was followed by a visit to the casualty department 19 miles away. There, I discovered that hospital X-ray machines were kept hidden in dull black boxes, and that radiographers retired behind screens when they took pictures.

In due course, I joined one of Father Oswald's physics classes. His X-ray machine was in frequent use, and I assisted at many demonstrations.

Father Oswald died of leukaemia in 1968.

A HARD-BITTEN irascible anatomist who is reputed to eat ignorant first-year students for breakfast, recently had occasion to change his newsagent. When the bill came it was addressed to him at the Department of Humane Anatomy. Since this tribute he has not been the same man. Our spies report that yesterday when someone was not attending in the osteology class he threw a humerus at the offender, though the femur was ready to his hand, and this morning he let a student through his viva on the skull first shot.

# IV

# General Practice

It has been said that every doctor is allowed one outstanding success. Mine occurred some years ago when I was working as a locum in the East End. An elderly man came to the surgery one evening with a mild stomach upset. He was very deaf and conversation was impossible. I communicated in sign language and by writing on odd bits of paper. After the main consultation was over, I thought to ask him about his deafness. It was no use, he said, he had had it for years. Nothing could be done. Despite his protests, I took out my auroscope to look at the eardrums. Both canals were clogged solid with wax. Without more ado, I took off my jacket and started to work. After some minutes of steady syringing he gave vent to a great shout which almost startled me out of my shoes. "I can hear!" he cried. "I can hear!"

The second ear followed and he left me with an almost beatific expression on his face. On the way out, he spoke to every patient in the waiting-room. About an hour later, there was a commotion outside the surgery door. My patient had brought round as many of his family as he could muster. He insisted they all shake me by the hand. "It's a miracle," said his wife. "Nothing but a miracle." By this time I was acutely embarrassed and with some difficulty managed to send them home.

Next evening, when I came to the surgery, there was a long queue of people waiting patiently outside the door. They were all deaf.

THE general practice in our district consists of an older doctor who is respected for his understanding and a younger man known for his scientific acumen.

A lady in her sixties had symptoms that always seemed to me to fit with hiatus hernia. So I was not surprised to hear that, after she had had a night of pain, the senior doctor had made this diagnosis. A few days later the pain recurred, more severely. This time the young doctor was on duty; he did an ECG and found evidence of infarction.

The lady's version was that the senior partner then called on her and manfully apologised for having made a mistake. She – equally decently – replied that this was unfair. "You see, doctor," she said, "I told Dr B much more than I told you. I told him the pain went down my left arm."

For several weeks she was treated for her coronary, but somehow did not improve as well as she might. So further investigations were ordered. From which the fitting conclusion emerged that both doctors were right.

Psychologically, the patient was delighted; her faith in each doctor was restored. But the most intriguing part of this story is the relief of public opinion. It would have been terrible if its assessment had been faulted.

I HAD never been suspected of salmon poaching before last week. And if it had not been for that stupid old faggot Miss Gossage, I would not be known to the police by now. We caught sight of her tottering across the bridge to deliver the parish magazines but we reckoned that she could not have seen us. We were crouching in the bushes on the bank of the beck, and the car was well hidden down the cart track to the old quarry. Fred got out the thick brown bottle, with the word "poison" moulded into the glass, removed the stopper, and remarked that this lot ought to do the trick. We tied the piece of gauze to a yard of cast from its neck and a length of strong twine, thence to the branch of a tree on the bank. We heaved the contraption into midstream. A gurgle of air bubbles, and the first part of our job was done, so we slunk back to the car and drove home.

It does not do to upset the feelings of local folk. We have enough sense to keep our mouths shut about what goes on in the rivers around these parts. It is all very well for the visitors to come here in their Jaguars and their natty check tweed suits, to knock back whiskies in the Anglers' Arms. They can stand in their thigh-length waders by the pool all day if they like, and fiddle about with fifty guineas' worth of fancy tackle, but if it's a nice bit of salmon you'd be wanting, just you knock at the back door of the roadman's cottage, or tip the wink at the garage. The younger men around the village reckon it is a bit square to go out with the gaff and the lantern: the 11+ and the bus to the county secondary school have opened the door to the chemistry laboratory for them. They can now get with it in a big way. The back of a Land-Rover holds more than a sack, and fish can be got to market a damn sight quicker and fresher.

Miss Gossage should have known better, but she told the vicar she was quite sure that no local people were mixed up in what she saw. So the vicar tipped off the water bailiff and he phoned for the police sergeant to hurry down below the bridge. The length of twine was pulled with care, the brown bottle bumped over the gravel to the bank, and the piece of dirty gauze broke surface. Our infernal device was unmasked. Wrapped in an empty cornflakes packet it has gone to the forensic science laboratory for analysis of the dregs in the brown glass bottle. The water bailiff and the sergeant lay for two long nights in the wet grass to nab us coming back. I felt rather sorry for them.

That is the trouble with public-health epidemiology in the field. It is so easy to upset one lot of people's feelings by trying to spare those of others. We should have scared the living daylights out of the whole parish if we had told them that, with the help of the Public Health Laboratory Service, we were quietly looking for typhoid carriers popping their sewage effluents into the beck, and it takes a nicely balanced bit of ballast to hold those gauze sampling swabs against the midstream flow without making it too difficult to haul them out again in a couple of days. An open empty drug bottle happens to serve the purpose. But just you try explaining to a water bailiff the difference between salmon and salmonella.

ALL was peaceful in our sitting room after morning surgery. The Senior Partner was busy practising his putting, attempting to hit his golf ball into an old metal urinal lying on the floor. Suddenly the Junior Partner spoke. "What we ought to do in this practice," he bleated, "what we really ought to do, is sell this old building and use the money for a swish new place on the Castle Farm estate." I am not a golfer myself, but I gather that, in order to control the direction of the ball to a certain extent, it is advisable to keep one's eye and one's mind firmly fixed on the business of getting club to impinge on ball; any distraction can, I believe, wreck the whole perform-ance. Certainly it seemed that the Junior Partner's remark did something to the stroke the old boy was making at the time, and I made a mental note to ask our practice manager to 'phone the builders about a new pane of glass for the window. The Senior Partner sighed heavily. "What, Tristram, is wrong with it?" he asked in the sort of voice I have heard patients use to one of our consultant surgeons when he has announced that he intends removing the vast majority of their internal organs. "It's old, it's dilapi-dated, it's unhygienic, and it's aesthetically unattractive," said the Junior Partner – I had to suppress the thought that he had just described the Senior Partner as well as the building, being quite fond of the old boy myself. The Junior Partner was warming to his subject. "We need a nice, bright, cheerful waiting area, with coffee and biscuits on sale, a crêche for the children, with toys and squash and things – it would encourage mums to come and bring their kids." "Who, in their right mind," said the Senior

Partner, "wants to encourage 'em? I've spent all my life trying to discourage them. And on the Castle Farm estate!" He shuddered, and so did I. Castle Farm is on the rough side – you know, the sort of place where even the rats run around in pairs. The Junior Partner launched into a long rigmarole about deprivation, and how they were All Like Us But Never Had the Opportunities We Had.

"I think it's a great idea, Tristram," I said, avoiding the horrified gaze of the Senior Partner, "and I have another one. You and Fiona have not found a house you like yet; well, we could incorporate a flat for you in the building, then Tarquin and Tabitha could go to the Castle Farm school and develop cross-cultural links which would be of inestimable value in forming their social consciences – make them first-rate citizens of the new world of tomorrow." I pushed the 'phone towards him. "Ring Fiona now," I urged. I bathed in the glow of admiration in the eye of the Senior Partner; we both know that Fiona is just a bit of an *arriviste*.

"Perhaps," said the Junior Partner, rather hoarsely, "perhaps it all needs a bit more thought, don't you agree?"

THE other day the Practice Car had to go to the garage. Needless to say it had not come back by the time surgery had finished, so I got into the Other One. That would not go either, so I upped the bonnet and made an examination. That did not get me very far, so having failed again with the emergency starter (alias starting handle), I advanced with plug-spanner and tommy bar at the present. As I did so the practice car drew up. My moment of revenge had come. Approaching the mechanic with a bright smile on my lips, the words came as sweetly off my tongue as I have ever heard them from any patient, "While you're here . . ."

THE practice is much concerned at the moment *in re* Jenkins. Personally, I think they all carry a share of the blame, Mrs Jenkins as much as anyone, and I do not feel the Junior Partner's contribution to the debacle is such that he can really afford to make the song and dance about it that he is.

When Mrs Jenkins saw the Senior Partner at 6.35 one evening and was told to go into one of our little examination rooms, undress and lie down, she had no business to fall asleep. Fair enough, the Senior Partner was remiss in forgetting all about her and going home, but had she stayed awake she could have called out before the receptionist locked up and left.

She would doubtless have slept till morning, had it not been for the Junior Partner. What possessed him to go into the surgery at 10.30 pm I will never know, though I suspect a certain disharmony in the home may have been the cause. Anyhow, in he went, and clattered around, waking Mrs Jenkins. Now it is not possible to wake in a strange bed, in a strange

38

room, in the dark and to get up and find a light switch without a certain amount of noise – which the Junior Partner heard. I am not sure what I would have done, but I suspect I would have remembered an urgent appointment and slipped quietly out. I am quite clear in my own mind that I would not have done anything so idiotic as to seize a club from the Senior Partner's golf bag and burst into the room whence the noise came; nor would I have shouted anything as juvenile as "You'd better come quietly!" The Junior Partner did both.

Mrs Jenkins was, understandably, not at her best, being thus faced by a strange man, in an unfamiliar room, while dressed only in a minuscule pair of panties – though I must add that, if rumour is to be believed, it was not a situation wholly outside her previous experience. Frankly, I consider it melodramatic to have fainted, and downright foolish of the Junior Partner to have caught her – let fainting women fall, is my motto, and then shout for a female member of staff to come and pick them up.

Not long before all this, Mr Jenkins slipped home from the pub, the harvest yielded by the electricity meter having been spent. Some feeble gleam of concern made him wonder why Mrs J had not returned from her visit to the surgery, so he rang the Senior Partner to inquire. This jogged the old boy's memory and they both went to the surgery. They arrived just at the moment the Junior Partner was holding an all-but-naked Mrs Jenkins in his arms.

Really, as I pointed out to the Junior Partner, when treating his black eye next morning, it was to our advantage that Jenkins had managed to get one blow in, as we could balance his threats of going to the General Medical Council with the fact that we had a case for assault against him – indeed, with his past record, a charge of grievous bodily harm and a spell in the nick was not impossible. But the Junior Partner is quite incapable of seeing it this way.

"The Problem of the Groom's Scalp. Ah! Now here is a case which might appeal to you, Holmes. I think it was in this case that all my faculties were exercised to their fullest extent, and I still look back on the case with satisfaction and regard its ultimate solution as one of my masterpieces. You will remember that after I qualified I went down to do a locum in Wales. The house was a dark gaunt building with an atmosphere of foreboding about it. The doctor's surgery was a dark musty room, and the only medical facilities I could find in it were seventy-nine rubber rings, a broken curved needle, and a pair of rusty nail pliers. Can you wonder that in these gloomy surroundings, and with few patients, the time hung heavy on my hands?"
"The solution is obvious, my dear Watson; you should have hammered the broken needle into the wall and passed the time trying to throw the rubber rings over it." "You amaze me, Holmes! That is exactly what I did. On the third day the monotony was broken by a telephone message from the

squire's house to say that one of his grooms had received a kick on the scalp, and he was sending him along to have it sewn up. You can imagine my chagrin, my dear Holmes. How in heaven's name was I to achieve a satisfactory closure of the scalp wound with the primitive equipment at my command?" "And did you manage it?" "It was really quite a trivial affair, Holmes. First of all I pulled out the needle from the wall and sharpened it to a crude point on the back doorstep. I then went upstairs and in the children's toy-cupboard I found an old ukelele from which I removed one string (the third, or F sharp if I remember rightly). Pausing to collect an old bottle of antiseptic that I had seen in the bathroom, I returned to the surgery; whereupon, I sewed up the wound with the ukelele string, holding the curved needle with the nail clippers, which I also used to cut off the ends of catgut." "You amaze me, Watson!"

A NEW and revealing light may be thrown on friends, colleagues, and the profession in general by study of the classified advertisements they insert in magazines so generously supplied by drug firms. By their small ads ye shall know them.

"Continental frame-tent, camp beds, &c, hardly used." One remembers the overbearing enthusiasm of only last year: "The only possible way to spend a holiday, old boy. Simply marvellous site amongst the pines just off the beach. We all adore it."

Evidently belief in the doctor's social prestige persists and the most tenuous connection may therefore bring commercial advantage. "Doctor's wife's cousin has delightful Afghan puppies for sale." Or, more usually, "Impoverished doctor's nephew seeks luxury flat at nominal rent."

The "GP locums vacant" columns may cause some revealing self-examination. No nights, no weekends. Do they really pay that much? There are the repairs to the car and the telephone bill. Yes, I will. It's no good. I'd never manage the obstetrics. Ah, here's one with no obstetrics. No good, it's just round the corner and my colleagues would find out.

"Mercedes Benz '300 SL'. Unwanted Christmas present. Will sacrifice" defies belief but is only a slight exaggeration.

"Medieval instruments of torture wanted. Also books on witchcraft, voodoo, &c.' That meek little dermatologist who never says a word at lunch. Who would have thought it?

"Wanted examination couch. State condition and price." So after all his moral rectitude about the virtues and delights of being full-time NHS he's planning to go private after all.

"For sale jodhpurs to fit 10-year-old, ballet shoes, ice skates hardly used." Someone else's daughter seems to be undergoing normal development.

ARE you sitting comfortably? Good! Then I'll begin. Once upon a time there was a doctor in the house who couldn't get out when he wanted to. In a moment of weakness this eminent consultant had offered to see two patients in a bit of time between an operating session and his outpatient clinic. "You can bring Mr X up now," he told his Girl Friday. "He's not . . ." she began but was mercifully saved by the bell. She hurried downstairs, fixed the usual welcoming smile on her face, only to find the front door would not open, despite her strenuous efforts and muttered threats. There was only one thing for it. She flipped up the letterbox and peered out. She was confronted by a large bristling overcoat. Even the buttons looked cross. Mr X pressed the bell again. Right in the poor girl's ear. It was a very loud bell too. So she yelled his name. He bent down and fixed her with a jaundiced eye. "What the devil . . ." he began. She explained. Mr X did not like what he heard. "Ridiculous! Can't stand here all day. I'm a busy man. You'd best go up and tell the doctor." She flew up the stairs again and breathlessly informed her lord and master of the situation. "Nonsense," said he. "It was perfectly all right when I came in", and he hurried down, only to be met with failure. Then began the first consultation by letterbox. In the end he instructed this impatient patient to go across to the hospital and wait there. "I'll get my girl to 'phone them and herald your approach," he promised. His secretary completed her mission. "Shall I send Mrs Y across too when she comes?" Her boss nodded. "I must go, or I'll be late for everything." "But how are you going to get out?" his Girl Friday asked wryly. "Easy," he replied. "The waiting-room window of course."

She stood there loyally holding his briefcase and watched him climb out on to the sill. From there, aided by a friendly drainpipe, it was but an easy stride on to the area railings. She leaned out and handed him the briefcase, and whether it was the small boy in him or happy memories of undergraduate days, he smiled for the first time that morning. He paused for a moment and nodded civilly to a couple of passing acquaintances passing beneath his feet, then jumped and was gone. Nobody seemed surprised to see him there.

His secretary had a romantic date that lunchtime, which she was determined to keep come hell or high water or jammed front doors, and when the time came for her to do the derring-do bit, she was managing very well and had just reached the vital step on to the railings when she heard a stentorian voice calling her by name, and beseeching her not to impale herself on those murderous spikes. She looked across the road and beheld a dear old doctor friend, now long-retired and very lame. And she watched in admiration as he waved his stick at the approaching traffic and hobbled to her rescue. Hero and Leander had nothing on him. They only had the Hellespont between them.

When she got back the locksmith was there and the door was open. "I've got some messages for you," he told her, "and those X-rays came. I put them on the table." The Girl Friday thanked him and smiled dreamily. Really, it had been quite a morning. "You know, you'd make someone a wonderful secretary," she said to the locksmith. And clutching the X-rays to her bosom in what could only be described as an act of utter sublimation, she floated upstairs to her office.

WHEN we spring-cleaned the cellar last week a paper dropped out of the back of a cupboard. It was a report on the finances and work done at the town dispensary during 1817 – a neatly printed balance-sheet of charitable and clinical detail, a glimpse at general practice in the second year after the battle of Waterloo.

The townsfolk who could not afford to buy their own medicines had to seek a letter of recommendation from a subscriber or the overseer of the poor. On one side of the balance-sheet the four duty surgeons subscribed half-a-guinea apiece. On the other side they received no fees. Only the apothecary got £80 salary a year. Medicines cost £148, and the total expenses for the year were £238.

1638 patients are on the list, with 1452 written off cured, 47 relieved, 62 dead, and only 77 carried forward to next year. The clinical material was varied: 248 cases of cowpox and only 55 of smallpox; 218 simple fevers against 73 typhus, 43 scarlets, and 5 choleras; 118 bothered with itch and 97 with worms. Interesting causes of death included "mortification of the toes in the workhouse". I can only hope that the cost accountants of the Department of Health never get hold of this document. I am not sure whose Waterloo it would be.

"Right," said the Senior Partner, helping himself to a third cup of coffee, "I think that brings the practice meeting to a close." He took the last ginger biscuit from the plate, and with an easy movement, born of long practice, dunked it in his coffee. "No one has any other business, have they?" It was a statement, not a question. "One moment," said the Junior Partner, "What about the burglar alarm system?" Exponents of the art of dunking ginger nuts will know that a smooth progression from cup to mouth is of the essence. An untimely interruption will impede the flow. Half of the biscuit dropped into the Senior Partner's cup, floated for a brief moment, then sank into the depths. The Senior Partner divided his look of distaste equally between his cup and the eager face of the Junior Partner, then gave a heartfelt sigh. "Go on, Tristram," he said. "Well," said the Junior Partner. "We *have* an alarm system, but it is never used. There are drugs on the premises, syringes, prescription pads. We really have a duty to be security-conscious . . ." He droned on.

He was not to know the problem when, in a fit of public-spiritedness, we had had it installed a couple of years ago. He was not to know that, every night for a fortnight, the wretched thing had gone off. The neighbours were very good about it, but the police were not so pleased after the fifth night in a row. The cleaning lady solved the mystery by pointing out that an internal door, which was fitted with alarm sensors, would blow open if the wind was in the right direction. So a lock was fitted to that door. But how was the cleaning lady supposed to know, when she locked up a couple of nights later, that the Senior Partner was in his room looking at the practice accounts and did not have a key to the new lock. Finding himself locked in, he let himself out by the rear door, rushed back in to shut off the alarm but found, alas, that the control panel was the other side of the newly locked door.

I have always maintained that it was sheer bad luck that neither of the men in the nearby police car were patients of the practice. Had they been, they would have recognised the Senior Partner and not greeted his attempts at self-identification with comments such as "Oh yes, and I am Father Christmas!" It was unwise of my colleague to use the language he did in reply. Things escalated, and, as the chairman of the bench pointed out the following morning, he most certainly should not have laid a hand on the arm of one constable, thereby committing a technical assault, nor invited him into the surgery with an offer to perform certain totally unnecessary endoscopic procedures on him. The matter was eventually hushed-up, but from that day, by common consent, the alarm has never been used.

The Junior Partner had finished speaking. The Senior Partner looked angry. Inspiration came to me. "Of course," I said, "the police will want one named person to be the keyholder and to turn out every time the alarm goes off – you will do that, Tristram, will you not?" The meeting closed soon after.

AWAKE! But it was not morning that had flung the stone into my Bowl of Night. It was young Perkins from The Golden Lion flinging pebbles at my bedroom window. Dad's face was cut something horrible, and would I come at once. The urgency of heading off old Perkins from the Dawn of Nothing penetrated my veil of sleep. Still befuddled, I pulled on my pants and jacket, picked up the emergency bag, and scurried along the street. Sure enough, the landlord was not a pretty sight. The takings from a rather wild party had included turning down an empty glass across old Perkins' refusal of yet another last round. He was sitting in the bar with a dish cloth clapped to his cheek. I reckoned it needed a fair few stitches to restore some sort of acceptable cosmetic effect. Mark you, Mr Perkins is not a fussy man about appearances: maybe twenty years of pub-keeping dulls the finer feelings. While the local anaesthetic was having time to act, I wandered round admiring the murals behind the bar. Gamecocks and racehorses to the left, cheesecake and pin-up girls to the right. Perkins was certainly a connoisseur of beauty. Thinking it was time to get on with the job, I leaned over the patient and inserted the first stitch. Perkins flinched. I wondered if the anaesthetic was all right. He said it was, so I pressed on. As I approached once more he drew back with a look of horror before the needle even touched him.

"What's the matter, Mr Perkins?" I snapped testily, "Surely it doesn't hurt? Why are you looking so scared?"

"Well, doctor," replied the victim. "Have you ever seen yourself without your teeth in?"

I glanced in the mirror over the bar. Indeed my dentures lay still in the Bowl of Night.

# V

# Doctor as Patient

*Doctor's thoughts on first days of his illness:* I'm not quite well – but it's really nothing.

*After a week:* I'd better treat it.

*A day later:* Maybe I should get some advice and get it investigated. I'll take a day off.

*Next day:* My doctor is taking this too seriously. I don't agree with his treatment. Let's see if I can get him to agree with me. After all, it's *my* illness! I'll soon be back at work anyway.

*A week later:* Well, at this rate I shan't be back very soon. I'd better do what he says. If I really am ill, I'd better act as if I am. After all I'm not indispensable. Perhaps this experience will give me some useful insights.

*A few days later:* It's not bad being at home and off work for a while. I can do just what I feel like doing – such as writing down this confession. It's good to see a bit more of the children, and to practise losing at chess in a naturalistic manner.

*A week or two later:* How can I stop my doctor trying to wrap me in cotton-wool after I've recovered? I suppose I could ring up a few friends till I find the right one to ask for a second opinion.

*Some days later:* My doctor doesn't need a second opinion, he says, because I'm now so unbearable that it's perfectly clear I've recovered. So he's letting me go back to work.

*After two hours at work:* I should have gone away for a holiday in the sun.

A CONSULTANT friend arrived home from hospital in a somewhat chastened mood. Being a patient for the first time was, to quote the jargon, a learning experience. An appendix which had grumbled for many years finally lost its temper and drove him into the arms of a surgical colleague with whom relations had been a trifle strained. My friend has the unfortunate habit of voicing criticisms loudly and without undue restraint. His remarks, while no doubt well intentioned, tend to arouse a variety of non-humanitarian emotions in the breasts of his colleagues.

Few would ignore the chance to seek a little revenge. Needles tended to feel blunt; there were persistent difficulties in obtaining a bedpan; his companion in the double-bedded bay was deaf and snored loudly; and there seemed to be a surfeit of enemas. Most satisfied was his senior surgical associate. Just before the operation he explained to his patient that normally he left appendixes to his juniors but, in this case, he would operate personally. My friend was wheeled into the theatre but a moment before the anaesthetic mask was applied he heard a loud voice saying, "Refresh my memory, sister. Is the appendix on the right or the left hand side?"

ALL day Sunday I had been feeling off colour; shivery, with muscle pain and a nagging discomfort below my right ear. Monday is an early-rising morning, and I became conscious of the noise of the alarm, and pain below and medial to both ears simultaneously. I stretched and yawned – and shut my mouth very quickly and hastily felt my jaws. After a horrified look in the mirror, I returned to bed announcing firmly that I was unfit for professional duties – and, no, I didn't know who was going to drive young Patrick to school.

A few hours later the family doctor confirmed the diagnosis of mumps by examination from the doorway and asked me if I knew the complications. He could be heard chuckling all the way to his car. Since then I have telephoned, or been telephoned by, about half a dozen colleagues, and have had the comments of perhaps a dozen more reliably reported. I have to record a high degree of sadism in the medical profession. This sadism may be overt, shown mainly by surgeons ("wait till the complications get you" theme); may be disguised as helpful advice, usually from physicians ("Heroic doses of wide-spectrum antibiotics *may* abort painful complications"); or may present as *Schadenfreude* in the uproarious Rabelaisian laughter of hearty GPs.

A NON-MEDICAL friend consulted a neurologist for an insurance medical examination. Knowing that he would be required to produce a specimen and mindful of previous feeble attempts in similar circumstances, he primed himself with coffee. He was therefore disconcerted to be offered a 20 ml bottle in which to provide "just a drop". This obligation was discharged without quite sacrificial dignity, continence, or the consulting-room carpet, and he left pondering upon whether this was a subtle test of moral fibre or of sphincter function. I thought it reflected the unwordliness of neurologists.

ONE is always a bit bashful about asking for blood tests on oneself – no one likes to be thought of as a hypochondriac. However, the margarine adverts having got to me and the latest atherosclerosis story beginning to look as though it might be true, I succumbed to the temptation of having my lipids done. Diffidently, I filled in the form: 40000 mile service, please. Alas, like my father before me, my cholesterol is high. The bio-chemist's comment was curt: Suggest oil change.

A WEEK or so ago, I was admitted to a London teaching hospital with what, after much doubt, was diagnosed to be a viral complaint affecting the joints of my wrists and fingers.

Yesterday it was considered that I was well enough to go home since all relevant tests had proved to be negative. I was sitting at the side of my bed waiting to be seen by the consultant rheumatologist, who eventually arrived accompanied by his entourage of half-a-dozen doctors and a ward sister. After a detailed examination, the consultant asked me how long I had had that black patch under the heel of my right foot. I answered that I did not know; I never looked under my feet. The patch was closely inspected by all present, and the consultant, turning to one of the doctors, instructed that it would have to be "dealt with".

The team moved on, and I, considerably distressed by what I had heard, carefully examined the dreadful black patch under my foot. Meanwhile, my daughter telephoned the hospital to inquire after my welfare and was informed of the discovery of the patch, which she immediately assumed was a bone cancer. Then I looked at the patch again, and putting a fingernail under one edge of it, peeled it away, to discover that it was nothing more dangerous than a manufacturer's label that had become detached from the inside of one of my bedroom slippers.

THE psychiatrist in a general hospital is usually a somewhat remote figure who appears at lunch and usually can be found talking about cars and income-tax and otherwise behaving like an ordinary human being. In a mental hospital the picture is very different. There, everyone strives to be well adjusted, well integrated, well rounded and never so hopelessly inadequate or insecure as to lose his temper or even show irritation with the more infuriating patients or colleagues. For ordinary mortals like myself these standards are rather exacting, but when I get home in the evening I find that when I have attacked the cat with a broom, cuffed our older child smartly behind the ear, shaken the younger till its teeth rattled, slammed down a charred sausage in front of my husband with a take-it-or-leave-it slant to my jawline, and ground the potato peelings savagely into the compost heap with my heel, I am refreshed and ready to be poised and sympathetic with my neurotics next day. It may be a bit hard on the domestic circle, but it's ever so abreactive.

# VI

# Call to Arms

*"I learned a lot in the Royal Army Medical Corps" makes a regular appearance as the opening lines of yet another episode in military reminiscence:*

I LEARNED a lot in the RAMC . . . For example, no matter how improbable, how far fetched, or how bizarre, always have an answer. In the Services, silence was taken as a sign of guilt and even the truth was usually suspect. The more ingenious the excuse, the more it was likely to be accepted. Not believed necessarily, but accepted.

One of my friends was charged with driving an Army car into a wall (his eyes had strayed to a passing blonde). He claimed he had been stung by a dormant bee and even had the puncture wound to prove it. (I had given him an injection into his gluteal region a day or so previously.) Another, accused of sounding a raspberry towards the end of a rather tedious lecture on ethics, escaped with but a minor reprimand when he explained that he was merely blowing away forcibly a fragment of tobacco leaf adhering to his lower lip.

The regulars, as might be expected, had a fine appreciation of the limits, the moves, and the responses of the game. For it was a game. A brigadier, inspecting my wards, told me to put the sergeant on a charge because there was a large cobweb near the ceiling. "Begging your pardon, Sir," said the sergeant. "Always keep a cobweb there. First-aid treatment to stop haemorrhage." "Charge dismissed," said the red-tabbed martinet. At the next ward, however, I was again ordered to put the sergeant on a charge. "On what grounds, Sir?" I inquired (I was very young!). "No cobweb on the ceiling," said the brigadier, looking at me severely.

. . . and to have a healthy but respectful scepticism about entrance medical examinations. Perhaps, in the days of National Service, there was a grain of truth to the views of the new recruits: if you walked in the door, said "Good morning" and were warm, you were fit. Not that it was ever as simple as that. However, I did come across a young infantryman with a glass eye. He said he confused the examining doctor by holding the card over his false eye each time he was asked to read the chart. His commanding officer said he was a first-rate marksman.

I once had to conduct an inquiry into why a handicapped youth had been called to the colours. I traced him to a large barracks where he was in charge of the telephone exchange, with the rank of lance-corporal. One leg was much shorter than the other, but this was compensated for by a special boot. How did he pass the medical, I asked? Quite simply, he replied. When the medical officer asked him why he was limping, he said he was only wearing one boot. His earnest plea that he be allowed to continue in his post until demobilisation was granted.

Not that I criticise either doctor or recruits. The lads I mentioned were young men who wanted to join the Army and were willing to go to some lengths to achieve their ambition. They were determined to prove they were just as able as their friends. For some, indeed, it was their first meaningful job. I often wonder if the examining medicos turned a blind eye to physical imperfections in the face of enthusiasm.

Of course, a few conscripts were somewhat the opposite. "Read that chart on the wall," said the major. "What chart?" asked the recruit. "Quite correct," said the examining doctor. "There is no chart. Passed for intelligence, eyesight, and quick wit."

. . . Amongst other things, how to adapt to the system. My best recollection of this came when my troops were suffering from a bad outbreak of influenza. Someone on high had a bright idea: anyone diagnosed as having influenza should have blood taken off immediately, with a further sample to be withdrawn six weeks later.

It was not accepted kindly as we were all run off our feet. My small hospital was filled to overflowing and two barrack rooms had been turned into temporary wards. Even the local Red Cross ladies had been drafted in to help with the nursing. Venepunctures and organising transport of specimens to the designated laboratory was the last straw. What to do? The solution was simple. I stopped diagnosing influenza. I think it is the only time in my experience where an epidemic was arrested as a result of an official letter. I have to say a new infection sprung up immediately. This was called "coryza with pyrexia". But, then, blood samples were not required.

. . . Amongst other things the shock of surprise. My ambulance and emergency care team were in attendance when a group of soldiers were clearing an old minefield. Progress was slow but steady as the sand was scraped away from the deadly contraptions before they could be made harmless. In the afternoon a brigadier came along to inspect the state of the operation. One sergeant just looked at him without springing to the salute. He was given a dressing down and the brigadier stormed off. Later, knowing the man, I asked him why the sergeant had not observed the proprieties. "I was paralysed," he said. "It was the first time I had ever seen an officer standing on a land mine."

ONE of the lessons which helped me greatly in my career as an administrative medical officer was the practice of the "dummy run". This is the technique of making an inspection an hour or so before the top brass arrives. On one occasion I found a poster saying nasty things about the Government, just minutes before a Ministerial visit. On another, a set of overflowing ashtrays under a "no smoking" sign in the ward duty room. Toilets without toilet paper and, indeed, without seats, have come to light before a visit by the chairman of the board. And expensive medical apparatus which should work but does not is commonplace.

The necessity for a dummy run was imprinted upon me when I was in sole charge of a small RAMC hospital. My tour took place a mere hour before a scourge from the War Office was due to appear. The recently posted sergeant pharmacist was adamant that there was no need to visit the rarely used isolation unit. I was just as determined that I should. Inside was an intricate array of flasks, filters, tubes, and bottles. A mixture of potato peelings, elixirs, and the preservative from pathological specimens was bubbling away at one end. Pure alcohol was dripping out the other.

In the event, I was commended by the general. He said the liberal use of carbolic acid, with its distinctive odour was highly appropriate for an isolation unit; and he was particularly pleased at the way I had stored a large quantity of broken glass safely in a cardboard box.

ONE afternoon, when regimental medical officer, I chanced to walk across the parade ground where the drill sergeant was training some new recruits. He halted the squad, stood them to attention, and brought them to the salute. He then approached me and, after saluting respectfully, drew to my attention, in a rather loud voice, my baggy trousers, dusty shoes, untidy tie, flopping trench coat with a button missing, and my thatch of ragged hair. "Sir," he said sorrowfully. "You must do better than that." He saluted and left. Red of face, I slunk past to the delighted and gratified silence of the square-bashing private soldiers.

Some weeks later the colonel ordered all ranks to take up cross-country running on Saturday mornings. Only those with a medical certificate would be excused. A queue formed outside my room the following morning. I cheerfully issued lines for all the middle-aged officers and senior NCOs, who suddenly discovered they had sore backs and bunions and took blackouts on strenuous exercise. The drill sergeant reported late in the day. He asked for a line on the grounds of his bad feet. I examined the offending members, battered by years of stamping on cement-hard parade grounds. I surveyed them, contemplated them, considered them, and pondered over them. At last I reached a decision. They were quite serviceable. I could not see my way to giving him a certificate. He looked me straight in the face: I looked him right back. We both understood the power of authority.

ONE also learned a semblance of the social graces. How to eat oysters as if they were fit for human consumption; what to do with the stones in a cherry pie when sitting next to a VIP (swallow them); how to eat spaghetti unselfconsciously; and to drink dry sherry instead of something pleasant.

I once made the *faux pas* of whistling in the mess between courses. In the dreadful silence which followed, I found the CO standing behind me. My spirited rendition of *The Dream of Olwen* faded into a sort of strangled ululation. The colonel spoke to me quietly for a few minutes, then left. I have to say that, thirty years later, I have never again whistled at table. Further, my two sons, now grown men, have never whistled when sitting down to a meal.

Sartorial detail was also something we were taught. Not so much the niceties of wearing a uniform – that was a lecture in itself – but how we should attire ourselves for sport, country, or town. This last involved a hat, a dark suit, a white shirt, and the famous broad-striped tie. In addition we were told always to carry an umbrella. As I had never possessed such an article, I decided to buy one when next in London. And this I did. It was an immaculate, thin, black pencil. The very epitome of the craftsman's art. I inquired how I should open and rewrap it. The assistant looked at me in horror. "One does not unfurl it, Sir" he said. "Never!" "What will I do when it rains?" I asked. "Quite simple, Sir," he replied. "Hold it out at right angles to the body and shout 'Taxi!'."

*Giles, of course, answered the call to serve his country. Both survived:*

LATE one evening Giles and I fell to reminiscing over our experiences in the RAMC. I had been posted deep into foreign climes – Dorset to be precise – and had difficulties with the language. I was also plagued by high-ranking officers who visited my little hospital with astonishing frequency. They outwitted me at every turn, revealing my cover-ups, with the casual insouciance which separates the true professional from the inspired amateur. Another bleak letter from the colonel!

Giles' passage was less eventful. He learned two valuable lessons during this time. If ever in trouble, he told me, before the superior officer could speak, Giles would ask with the innocence of a mere National Serviceman, what was the meaning of the first ribbon on the chest facing him. By the time this was explained, usually in terms of modesty, pride, and throw-away understatement, he was rarely given more than a passing admonishment. His second lesson, and would that I had learned it too, was when to say the right thing. Towards the end of our basic training, the commanding officer held a "grouse" meeting. We all had our say. The food was uneatable – and worse, there was not enough of it. The beds were like boards – and worse, we had to rise too early. The drill sergeant was rude to us – and worse, we could not answer him back. As the session was drawing to a close, Giles rose to his feet. He praised the CO for guiding us through a difficult and traumatic time; for teaching us the traditions of the Corps; and for taking such a personal interest in our dress, conduct, and general well-being. He sat down to an enthusiastic, if somewhat mystified, round of applause. One week later, we were all given notice of the far-flung places to which we had to proceed forthwith. Giles was posted to the War Office with the immediate rank of major.

# VII

# "Is there a Doctor . . .?"

WHEN my wife and I go down to Devon for a long weekend, we always go for a meal at a favourite seafood restaurant. Inevitably the proprietor discovered our respective professional backgrounds, though he never took advantage. One wet, dark evening out of the season, we were the only diners in the place, and the proprietor was preparing to close. Suddenly the door burst open, and in came a dishevelled man in shirtsleeves and soaked to the skin. Breathlessly he announced that he needed help. His wife was very pregnant, extremely distressed, and screaming. The proprietor, all concern, interrupted to reassure him that all was now well; pointing to us he revealed that I was a doctor and my wife a midwife. We felt distinctly worried, neither of us having been involved with deliveries for over twenty-five years. But all was well. The man tersely explained that he did not require a doctor or a midwife. He wanted a seafood establishment. His wife had this uncontrollable craving for a crab sandwich; would the proprietor please stop wittering and produce one?

THE Northern Line has greatly helped my adult education. I tend to read *The Lancet* slowly and obsessively, and without my daily journey to the hospital I would never get through it. But there are snags. Before leaving in the morning I fold my *Lancet* so that the first article is outermost – I am not going to make things too easy for the peripatetic occupation-spotter.

Page 1 is a solid mass of small print and as there are no pictures my neighbours remain buried in their papers. Page 2 is still a mass of print, but there on page 3 is an article on "Four Cases of Virilism in the Adult Female". It is well illustrated and I quickly turn over. Still virilism – cases 3 and 4 look more advanced with larger illustrations. The breathing down my neck has increased to gale force. Knowing the hormone expert's penchant for close-ups I take no chances and now turn over two pages at once. Here I am safe. No pictures except a photomicrograph which looks like an enlarged view of porridge. I try to continue reading, but as I have not the courage to turn to the beginning of the article I cannot understand a word and wonder if I dare turn over again. I have a vague recollection that when I received the journal there was somewhere in it "Anencephaly with Survival for Four Days", with a photograph on each day.

I am writing a paper for *The Lancet*'s next educational number on "Good Illustration as an Obstacle to Medical Teaching".

WE had been taken to the theatre; towards the end of the last act our host began to sweat and look pale. After enduring the National Anthem I guided – supported rather – him away from the general scramble to the exits and stretched him out over some seats in the stalls. I then started to wonder what might be amiss and whether I was really the man to cope with the situation. At that moment a man approached stating that he was a doctor and offering help. Much relieved I handed over without a word. Then I began to foresee our mutual embarrassment if events should develop in a way which would force me to reveal my professional identity. Very humbly I said how grateful I was, since I was only a surgeon. "So am I," he said, and departed.

MY long-planned talk on Reassurance has been brought one step closer by a summer-holiday incident. It was a warm Sunday morning and the queue of cars waiting to cross Windermere by the Bowness ferry was longer than usual. But time did not press and I composed myself to benevolent patience. The ferry came in, the cars drove on, and the rest of the queue began to move slowly forward. Only the car immediately in front of me stayed resolutely put. Presently the lady driver got out looking rather anxious and came up to my window.

"I'm afraid the old lady's collapsed on me," she said.

I thought, what an endearing way to refer to the faithful family jalopy. It was no vintage model, but certainly past its prime. Being non-mechanical and unable to recognise anything bigger than a bee under a bonnet, I could not offer help, but I wanted her to know that I was content to remain parked behind her until the old lady was prepared to move again.

"Never mind," I said, with a Reassuring smile.

She looked non-Reassured and got back into her car. I then noticed that she had a passenger. An old lady. And as far as one could tell from her back view, the old lady had indeed collapsed. I leaped out of my car and went round to the nearside window. The old lady was ashen grey, her head drooped on her chest. Through the window I picked up her cold hand and felt for a pulse. Not a flicker.

The moment of truth. This is when I wish I was a boy scout. I should know just what to do. Old lady apparently dead in the car. Three children just behind in mine. Many more cars behind that, all beginning to look restive. The lady driver felt for the other pulse and looked more anxious than ever. She clearly needed Reassurance.

"I'm a doctor," I explained.

"So am I," she confessed.

The old lady's eyelids flickered. I noticed that she was breathing – now and then. A little colour returned to her cheeks. Presently she raised her head, opened her eyes, looked at both of us, and summed up the situation.

"I shall be all right now, thank you," she said with a small smile.

It was very Reassuring.

OUR local professor of pathology has run into some embarrassment again. One sunny Sunday's evening he was called out urgently to see a stricken neighbour. Grabbing his aged stethoscope from the bottom of the roll-top desk, he ran to the scene of the catastrophe, but the old lady was obviously dead. The curious and fearful onlookers seemed to expect some sort of doctor performance and he made to listen with the tubes. Alas, the black rubber had set hard in its windings; it fractured into a myriad pieces and, as the professor said afterwards, "bounded over the floor like liquorice allsorts".

He appeared in the bacteriology department early on Monday to ask for some plastic tubing that would not fracture. We gave him a length of our own cheap and nasty, but so pathetic was his gratitude that we hadn't the heart to tell him that it becomes extremely sticky with age.

WHEN in London recently I chanced upon a small group of people gathered round an elderly lady who was propped up against some railings. She had fallen and damaged her ankle. As I was about to volunteer my help I heard a transatlantic voice say, "There is a doctor's house nearby. I saw it myself. If we carry the lady up that street into Gough Square we can find it." Just then an ambulance drew up and whisked the casualty away to hospital.

As I passed the former house of Dr Samuel Johnson (1709–84) with its circular blue plaque I wondered what he would have said to James Boswell (1740–95) if a lady with a broken ankle had appeared on his doorstep.

WHAT would Dr Samuel Johnson have said if a lady with the injured ankle had been brought to his door? The response might not have been as unfavourable as one might expect. Boswell describes Johnson as a "great dabbler in physic" although he showed some contempt for the almost universal practice of bleeding. The *Life of Samuel Johnson* contains the following prescription for relief of rheumatism: "Equal quantities of flour of sulphur and flour of mustard-seed to be made into an electuary with honey or treacle". This mixture was to be taken as a bolus "as big as a nutmeg", to be followed by a quarter pint of infusion of lovage root. The letter also contains the modest admission: "my opinion of alternative medicine is not high . . . if it does harm, or does no good, it may be omitted; but that it may do good . . . is desired by, Sir, your most affectionate, humble servant, Sam Johnson." I am rather tempted to include this last phrase in my outpatient letters.

*And before we leave that famous "doctor":*

WHY did Dr Samuel Johnson leave his comfortable life in London to trot off around Scotland's Western Isles with Boswell in 1773? After all, he was well past sixty and his health was not good. Boswell's engaging personality was one reason. Another was that Dr Johnson's curiosity had been long aroused by reading Martin Martin's curious little book *A Description of the Western Islands of Scotland*. I was lucky to get a copy recently, and very strange reading it is. There is much in it of interest to a physician. Here, for example, is Martin's account of what one is tempted to call hammer therapy:

"There is a Smith in the Parish of Kilmartin, who is reckon'd a Doctor for curing Faintness of the Spirits. This he performs in the following manner: The Patient being laid on the Anvil with his Face uppermost, the Smith takes a big Hammer in both his Hands, and making his Face all Grimace, he approaches his Patient; and then drawing his Hammer from the Ground, as if he design'd to hit him with his full Strength on the Forehead, he ends in a Feint, else he would be sure to cure the Patient of all Diseases: but the Smith being accustom'd to the Performance, has a Dexterity of managing his Hammer with Discretion: tho at the same time he must to it as to strike Terror in the Patient: and this they say has always the design'd Effect . . ."

Is this so far removed, I wonder, from giving the right number of shocks nowadays with our much more elaborate ECT apparatus?

# VIII

# In Committee

THE story is going the rounds of our hospital's new manager being telephoned in the middle of the night. A voice, definitely slurred, demanded to know when the outpatient department would open. "Nine o'clock," snapped the great one, slamming down his telephone. Twenty minutes later he was again jerked from his well-earned repose. The inebriated caller asked the same question. "It will still open at nine," yelled the irate iron chancellor, "but I doubt if they will let you in, in your condition." "Don't want in," replied the voice, "want out."

MEDICINE is certainly expanding its spheres of care. This morning I read about a doctor who worked for "the embryonic mental health team" of a certain hospital; obviously they believe in the value of early treatment. At the other extreme, by the same post I received a copy of a Ministry of Health report of a symposium on the Care of the Dying. I was fascinated, on reading the table of contents, to find, just before the list of those present, a "list of bodies represented".

WITH the approach of a new committee season, a number of postulants will shortly be making their first wide-eyed entry into the Big Time, their gaze perhaps already fixed on the next step into the veritable corridors of power. They will not know – nor should they be asked yet to believe – that the corridors have no direction and no effective end. The diligent and steadfast explorer may, it is true, finally be led to the awareness of a not-unfriendly emptiness; and those who are especially perceptive and persevering have claimed that they occasionally hear somewhere in the emptiness the fleeting echoes of distant laughter.

Comic as it may appear against the background of more heroic achievements, the committee remains the only known alternative alike to unbridled authoritarianism and to unbridled democracy. Neither alternative has so far shown itself to be an effective means of generating corporate professional thought, and an understanding of the niceties of committee expression is therefore as essential a piece of equipment as a stethoscope. The following glossary will provide newcomers with some small guidance as to what is actually being said in committee.

| COMMITTEE ENGLISH | PLAIN ENGLISH |
|---|---|
| This is surely a matter of principle | This involves money |
| This is surely a matter of high principle | This involves a lot of money |
| Those of us who are in real contact with patients | The BMA's GP committee |
| The profession at large | *ditto* |
| The people of these islands | *ditto* |
| Our general practitioner colleague | That blackguard of a GP whose name I can never remember |
| Our friend from the regions | That unspeakable hick from somewhere beyond the Green Belt, whose name I certainly won't admit to knowing |
| We're always grateful for a breath of fresh Northern air | These bloody Scots |
| Our very valued delegate from the junior staff | That sickening young upstart whose name I have very carefully noted |
| I'm sorry I have to challenge the accuracy of para 147 of the minutes | Para 147 is an accurate account of the committee's having once again failed to appreciate my point of view |
| On a point of order | In the hope of prolonging the present disorder |
| The accurate conceptualisation of these modalities subsumes a parameter for the predicated monitoring of the viability of | I have recently been on a lecture tour in the United States |

59

| | |
|---|---|
| this committee's contribution to our professional ethos as of at this time | |
| I take the point | What a load of rubbish |
| I should be most happy to support the vice-chairman's candidature for this important additional office | The bastard |
| I agree with almost everything the last speaker has said | I agree with nothing the last speaker said |

OUR district NHS headquarters are in what was, in its day, a very grand house. The architectural pièce de résistance is the ballroom, and from its high ceiling hang three magnificent chandeliers of hand-cut glass. They are reputed to be priceless, and over the years have lent an aura of importance to the discussions going on underneath.

Now there is one snag about this ostentatious display, and that is that periodically the chandeliers have to be cleaned by a specialist whose account runs into four figures every time. Recently, after making all possible cuts in such unimportant areas as nurse staffing, medical equipment, and so on, it became clear that some economy would be necessary at HQ. Our new leader did not flinch; he ordered the works department to clean the chandeliers themselves.

So, after a lengthy discussion on methodology, a scaffold tower was hired and duly delivered to HQ. A couple of hours hard work saw it erected adjacent to the first chandelier and, before starting on the actual cleaning, it was decided to have a refreshment break. The men shinned down the tower and made for the door – only to be halted in their tracks by a curious creaking noise behind them. They looked back. Somehow the tower had not been properly erected and, in the slow-motion reserved for nightmares, waking or sleeping, it collapsed gracefully to the ground – taking with it one priceless and irreplaceable chandelier.

THE procedure to be followed in the event of a bomb threat in these offices reads: "After being alerted that a bomb threat has been received, anyone wishing to evacuate, irrespective of the decision for a total evacuation, may do so voluntarily after notifying his/her head of department. Upon evacuation, staff members should assemble in Hyde Park (near Rotten Row) . . . Evacuation should be by the staircase and *not* the lifts."

Before the NHS purchased a well-known sanatorium for conversion into a rehabilitation unit, an architect was sent to inspect the fabric, and he brought with him an employee of a local firm armed with hammer and chisel to do the dirty work under his direction. They discovered dry-rot in one of the wooden buildings, and this the vendors had to make good before the buildings changed hands. The local firm was told to get on with it. The bill that they rendered was staggering. It specified in detail not only the timber used and the employee's hours on the job but also items such as his travelling distances, contributions towards his holiday pay, hire and depreciation of tools employed, and a whole lot more, totalling more than £90. When the vendors, who had dealt amicably with the local firm for many years, rang them up expostulating, they were told, "Oh, we thought we were working for the NHS. That is how we are instructed to render our accounts. Sorry, our mistake. Send it back and we'll send you a revised account."

A few years later, when the rehabilitation unit was well established, the word got round that the region's annual expenditure was not fully mopping up its allocation, and the surplus had got to be spent; otherwise next year's allocation would be cut. A sizeable sum was therefore spent on fitted carpets in all rooms and corridors and similar luxuries which could only be regarded as patient-therapeutic in the broadest sense: luxuries which generations of private paying patients had managed to get along without quite happily for half a century. Is not all this a bit cockeyed when the supply of dialysis machines is less than adequate?

Our former lady chairman had a heart of gold. This was never better demonstrated than when she led a visitation to our local hospital. A small boy was sitting in the waiting area, beside his mother, crying miserably. Apparently his brother was being admitted. Our chairman crossed over to comfort him. But nothing would cheer him up. Even making the accompanying board members talk to him had no effect. It was all to no avail.

Eventually, with the mother's permission, she coaxed him into joining the deputation. He toured the hospital alongside her and at every ward she took him up to say hello to the patients. Some gave him little presents; others, the ladies, a simple hug and kiss. When, at last, they returned to his mother he was a different child. Bright and cheerful, his pockets were stuffed with sweets and nuts. In his hand he held a large bar of chocolate. It was at this point that I joined the party. "Isn't he the happy boy, now," said our chairman, telling me the whole story. "Indeed, he is," I replied. "In fact," I continued, looking at him closely, "I doubt if I have seen a happier child with chickenpox in all my professional career."

MY grandmother, a shrewd Geordie lady, had a theory that if trade in the restaurant was slack, then slow, soothing music was played to ensure leisurely eating and so keep the place looking well-patronised; on the other hand, if the restaurant was busy and prospective diners were being turned away, then, she believed, orders went out to play *molto furioso*, with the result that everyone ate in time to the music (and consequently got indigestion) with the waitresses running about to match, thus producing increased customer throughput.

She may well have been right. If so, then the facility has been lost through the use of magnetic tapes or compact discs. Some restaurants try to improve their image by playing popular classics. This can have its pitfalls, my wife and I once being reduced to hysterics as we struggled to eat roast leg of lamb to the accompaniment of Bach's *Sheep may Safely Graze*.

If my grandmother's theory was correct, what an opportunity our hospital administrators are missing! Could not suitable music hurry up nursing procedures? Aptness should also be considered – musically knowledgeable people could make appropriate suggestions. For a start, however, I suppose *Unto us a Son is Given* from the *Messiah* would suit roughly half of the maternity ward. Perhaps *Barber of Seville* in the surgical wards would cause offence to the surgeons, and the repeated *motif* of the *Toy Symphony* might be tactless on the psychiatric unit – but it would have to be the *Nutcracker Suite* for neurosurgery. What about dermatology? *Patience*, perhaps? Then there would be the choice of an accompaniment to the professorial grand round. Unless things have changed since my student days, I would suggest *Music for the Royal Fireworks*.

A THORNY and complex problem has been resolved in our area, and represents a triumph of the spirit of determination to overcome all difficulties. I refer, of course, to the matter of the light bulbs.

When a light bulb expires, the procedure is for a requisition form to be completed (giving the site and nature of the fault and confirming that the faulty part remains available for inspection). This form is conveyed to the works department which, in the fullness of time, sends out an electrician to check that the bulb has indeed failed. Assuming his report corroborates the original requisition a second visit will be made, a new bulb inserted, tested, and, all being well, commissioned. This system works well in the main hospitals where, without wishing to boast, it is possible for the process to be completed in a shade over twenty-four hours.

In one of our small longstay units, however, way out in the country, the above procedures are not so effective. For a start, requisitions are collected only weekly and visits from maintenance staff are of like frequency. Thus, a couple of weeks can pass before a bulb is replaced. Some months ago the idea was mooted that, if a small supply of bulbs was available, staff would be prepared to do the job themselves. This proposal had far-reaching implications, of course, and had to be considered at length in many a committee. Questions were raised, however, under the Health and Safety at Work Regulations, as to the advisability of nurses changing light bulbs. The senior nursing officer (planning) and the senior nursing officer (education) devised an in-service training course in the changing of light bulbs. This short course covered all aspects of practical technique, without going into great detail on the theory. Selected senior nursing staff were sent on this course and, at the end, were given a short practical test. It is a matter of pride that the pass rate was 100%, and both of them are now deemed to be capable of changing a bulb if the delay of waiting for an electrician is unacceptable, and they alone have access to the bulb store. It is believed that this development will excite great interest throughout the NHS, and it is possible that the course will be made available to staff throughout the region – even nationally.

SPIRITS ran high when we started to plan our new medical school and ward block. There were eager faces when we inspected the plywood mock-ups and knitted brows as we debated the merits of lecture theatres and multi-discipline laboratories. Fifteen years, 2 area reductions, 3 cost reductions, and 7 revisions later, with the turf still uncut, enthusiasm is waning. To restore the flagging interest of our colleagues we have devised a new game – Medschool Monopoly. It is played on a shrinking board and you deduct £200 every time you pass "Go". There is endless scope for inventing new hazards in the "Chance" pack. "Throw a six or your room will be turned into a lift shaft." "Your office moves to beside the toilets; sound-proofing disallowed." "Remove 21 power points without offending colleagues." "Site same equipment in half the lab area without overloading ring mains." "Run services duct through professor's office." "Delete venetian blinds from south-facing window."

At first we did not have a "Go to jail" square, reasoning that there is no more innocuous pastime than building educational castles in Spain, but we have replaced it as we became more adept at dodging the regulations, disguising counters as deepfreezes to get them on the maintained supply. You can buy the whole set, complete with loaded dice, for less than it costs to turn a single gas point into a double.

I FOUND our group engineer in a cellar under one of my smaller laboratories. I told him that I had just seen men carefully stacking steel pipes on the lawn in front of the windows of the room where the hospital management committee meets. He murmured something about an unfortunate misunderstanding, but I know him better. "Are those the pipes that you would use to relay the main services between the blocks?" I asked. He nodded. "That's the job that you wanted to do next year, but which may now be put off by the building and works subcommittee."

"Yes, but within three months they will be so sick of the sight of those pipes, obstructing their precious view and spoiling their beautiful sward, that they will tell me to get on with the job."

"You should not monkey with the committee's decision."

"I am not monkeying with their decision, Doc. I am carrying out my long-term maintenance programme, which they have already approved. Since I learned to manipulate the bureaucratic machine, life has been less frustrating."

REORGANISATION at our hospital has produced a splendid improvement in the arrangements for getting into the pharmacy out of hours. The key used to be kept on the second shelf on the right, just inside the door of the old larder in the medical officers' quarters. The door was kept double-locked and only those privileged with the grand master key could get at it. This arrangement worked awfully well because the medical officers' quarters were next door to the pharmacy, and everyone knew that the pharmacy key was in the old larder where it had been kept for as long as anyone could remember.

But now things are much better. The key in the old larder is no longer the pharmacy key but the key to a little cupboard in the telephonists' office at the front entrance, and the pharmacy key is in the little cupboard. So if you want to get into the pharmacy after hours now, you first walk down to the old larder, unlock the door, get the little key, walk for five minutes to the front entrance, unlock the little box, get the pharmacy key, walk five minutes back to the pharmacy, get what you want, then walk back five minutes to the front entrance, replace the pharmacy key in the little box, lock it, then walk back to the old larder in the medical officers' quarters, replace the little key, then double-lock the old larder door.

# IX

# Doctor Abroad

TIME was when my gate lodge was tenanted by a lady with an absentee husband. In Ireland this is quite usual, as the breadwinner goes to Britain to earn a better wage. The frequent presence of bicycles against the lodge wall indicated a lively social life, but I thought little of it until one morning I found a solitary character moodily roaming around the empty lodge. His wife, it seemed, had flitted. It appeared that "herself" had been running a flourishing house of ill-fame under the unwitting umbrella of the gynaecologist, her landlord. The house-agent, a desiccated and disillusioned gentleman, overhearing my tale to his clerk, peered over his glasses from his desk and said, deadpan, "Doctor'll be looking for something for the goodwill."

I SHOULD like to say Giles spent his summer holidays cruising on the Rhine, or following Stevenson's travels in the Cévennes, or fishing for salmon on the Spey, or even taking a conducted tour of the vineyards of France. But this would not be true. He left it so late that we all ended up in a concrete jungle, a mile from an overpopulated beach on the Costa Dinero.

Once the initial shock wore off we came to enjoy it. Indeed, Giles claimed that, once he had deafened himself with cottonwool, the vibrations from the disco below were quite soporific. He soon found a little café run by two expatriate English ladies who made an acceptable cup of tea. They even had a special open air breakfast of ham and eggs, hot buttered toast, and marmalade. Giles made his way there every morning, returning with a satisfied air to the deckchair we had reserved for him under the large striped umbrella near to the cool drinks bar.

Giles said his Spanish improved no end when the young lady in the bikini started to speak to him. It ended abruptly when he was made to practise his French on an undertaker from Lille. The evenings were a particular delight. We sat at a pavement café, under the stars, drinking coffee and liqueurs, sampling some of the over-rich gateau.

When we returned home, a colleague asked him how he had enjoyed his holiday. "A memorable experience," said Giles. "We stayed at a small hacienda not far from the shore and ate at a local taverna. The food of the country is always best, you know. Black bread, paella and stewed squid washed down with a rough red wine. A bit primitive, of course, but how else can you get to know a country?" "What about that postcard you sent me," said our colleague: "it showed a large hotel and a swimming pool." But Giles did not seem to hear. He was lost in a reverie.

THE "Land-Rover" was leaking, badly; we only just made it between one water-hole and the next, and its bubblings were horrid to see. The long Indian road stretched away between the mango trees; it was a very hot day. The man on the stretcher in the back – he had a fractured cervical spine – said nothing; it was probably bliss for him when the rattling wheels came to rest whilst we scooped up water in the cigarette tin. His brother and mother, sitting on the floor of the vehicle, said nothing; they probably knew about cigarette tins of water being necessary for motors. But the two Englishwomen who were taking turns at driving – and the cigarette tin – said quite a lot. One had just come from Africa and there you put in soap, if possible carbolic soap; it settled down over the leak and got you home. The other had lived in India for a long time and always had used white of egg. A village; we stop. I find a tiny stall with a very large Punjabi merchant in it and he sells aspirins and iron pyrites, cough lozenges and soap, long bars of dry but strong-smelling carbolic soap. I get back to the vehicle first and feed it liberally with good red lumps, fill up from the well, and wait to drive away. But now my companion comes back, with an egg, the gift of a grateful patient; a very small egg indeed and grossly discoloured. Villagers crowd around us: we separate yolk from white and into the radiator goes the albumen; there seems very little of it. We are off; we are cured; we do not leak. I gingerly step up the speed and all is well; we are glad, for the fractured spine needs a hospital bed badly; perhaps I speed up a little too much; yes, I have. We arrive at the hospital gates with a bang; we have blown our top and look what is boiling out – a splendid scarlet foam, rich and red and apparently never ending; it spreads over the bonnet, it seeps into the dust.

SUMMER is icumen in, and mens sana in corpore sano is openly ignored. You are ready to go on holiday. Are you prepared for the psychosomatic disorders of rapid change in times, for the discomforts and discourtesies in hotels, foreign and domestic? If you are not, why go? Probably because of family or social pressures, or both. If you don't go, people will say you can't afford it – an intolerable accusation – or that you must remain on the job for fear of losing it. The one unacceptable thesis is that you like what you have at home and see no reason to leave it. My proposed international enterprise, "Holidays Surrogate", will take care of the entire matter, on a strictly confidential basis. Thus, you may visit any place you wish for as long as you wish, all without going there. Let's suppose that you have announced a fortnight's visit to the Mediterranean in mid-season. On a sound-film projector, lent by us, you will see the crowded airport waiting-room, with the exasperated travellers, and will hear frequent announcements of delays in departure. Next come scenes in the aircraft with all the noises made by passengers and crew. The film will include the traffic congestion at the pebbly beach. Here, additional notes of authenticity are available: you open a sealed plastic bag, its contents a sample of the refuse deposited by the joyful throng. As the camera approaches the water's edge, you unseal the flip-top can and shake its contents, thus releasing the smells from the mixture of seawater, fuel oils, and other unmentionable material. This should give a good idea of what you are missing. But not everything on a holiday is bad. What about that little restaurant you alone are sure to have discovered? We will send you, frozen, whatever that little restaurant served which would have sent you into ecstasies. Then, too, there is a good assortment of underexposed and overexposed snapshots of appropriate scenes. Our fees? A modest percentage of the costs given by any reputable travel agency.

THE trawler gave us a call at midnight to say that the bosun had injured his hand. We made a rendezvous at the mouth of Tafnafjord at first light. The bosun was over six feet in height and built in proportion. A projecting strand on a wire rope had lacerated his index finger and penetrated his middle finger. The laceration was not severe, but needed stitches. The middle finger was swollen and tender, and potentially infected. When I packed my gear to go across I had visualised a civilised little operation. I then discovered that all our local anaesthetic was of the wrong sort. The stitching was therefore done in the best tradition of marine surgery: the bosun was given half a tumbler of neat rum. I declined the offer of similar premedication and set to work. It was a crude business since the skin on his calloused hands was about a quarter of an inch thick. The suturing was followed by a jab of penicillin, and then the bosun arose. "Skipper," he said, "was that my daily tot, or do I still have one to come?" "No, Frank," said the skipper, "that was doctor's orders. You'll get your tot." I left strict instructions for three days of oral penicillin and three days' rest for the hand. As the trawler was newly out from home I did not get my customary basket of fresh fish. Next day we inquired on the radio, "how's the bosun?" "He's working on deck" was the reply. I could only echo the hackneyed phrase, "Keep on with the tablets."

WHY don't I keep my big mouth shut? Since birth I have been 100% tone-deaf: my nursemaid winced at the discords, the kindergarten mistress asked me not to sing in the carols, the French master tore his hair. Consequently all foreign languages are beyond me. I haven't a clue what all those mouthings mean without the explanatory gesticulations. But when in Rome, or Stockholm, or Oslo, I really do try to merge into some of their less exotic background habits. On a visit to a large camp of young people I was invited to dine at the top-table on the first evening. With punctilious courtesy we stood behind our chairs until the whole company was assembled in the dining hall. The commandant gave three sharp raps on the table with his knife, and spoke a couple of dozen words in Norwegian. Everyone bowed their heads and looked most solemn. I said "Amen" rather loudly and sat down. It seemed the obvious way of joining my hosts in spirit, but the top-table looked distinctly startled. For want of anything better as an opening conversational gambit, I leaned across to our interpreter and inquired if the commandant's words were the usual form of Norwegian grace. When the howls had died down, I gathered the horrible truth of his translation "If you want any beer you must buy it yourselves."

WHEN I was at school, I was much taken with the problem of how the Australians managed to conduct their affairs while suspended upside down. Sir maintained that they were not really upside down at all, but I was never convinced by this ex-cathedra statement.

Nowadays, when I visit Australia frequently, my original picture of Australian postural problems has been strongly reinforced. For example, for a few days after my arrival I have a fuzzy feeling in my head which is different from mere jet lag, such as I experience in the northern hemisphere; I can only attribute it to a readjustment of the blood supply to prevent pooling in my brain.

Other phenomena corroborate my bodily inversion. The sun, which in Britain is wont to travel sedately from left to right as you look at it, in Australia rides round the course from right to left, causing untold alarm and despondency; at night the moon behaves in the same unnatural fashion. It is not seriously to be supposed that something has happened to the sun and moon, and only one explanation satisfies the facts: the Australians are upside down.

The shape of the moon confirms this. The Romans used to call it *luna mendax*, the lying moon, since when it was waxing (*crescens*) it was shaped like a D, and when waning (*decrescens*) it was shaped like a C. Anything in the nature of a Latin mnemonic to describe its behaviour was thus nullified. But in Australia the waxing moon is C-shaped, and the waning moon is D-shaped; here it is a truth-teller, not a liar. These shapes can be reversed if the observer stands on his head, and the conclusion is once again inescapable: the Antipodes and their inhabitants must be upside down.

It is therefore quite a relief, both physiologically and psychologically, to step on to the tarmac at Heathrow and find myself once again the right way up. But I do wish that the wretched place was less overcrowded and impersonal, and that it had a supply of Australian sunshine.

# X

# Finding a Rhyme

### SWOTTING IN THE SUN
*(after Louis MacNeice)*

Atopic Ann was thought to be a sixth-form high achiever
But pollen from the mowing grass in June brought her hayfever;
It's no go with weeping eyes when you can't express your
    knowledge
And its no go for medical school or a place at an Oxbridge
    college.

It's no go my honey-love; it's no go my poppet;
June is the month for the GCE: the teachers will not swap it.

It's no go sitting Higher Maths taking antihistamine
And Spoken French with a blocked-up nose is clearly not your
    scene;
You can hope for the best with steroid drops and injections
    prophylactic
But it's on the cards that you'll get two Cs and go to a
    Polytechnic.

It's no go my honey-love, it's no go my poppet;
Atopics sit their exams in June: there is no way to stop it.

### SONNET ON HEM-LINES

That time of year thou may'st behold in me
When gold supplants the green in summer's leaf:
Should I feel now an extra-systole
'Twould not be for a mini-skirt too brief.
In me thou seest the embers of a fire
That on the ashes of his youth doth rest:
Who watched hem-lines progressively go higher,
Alas! with academic interest.
Yet, I applaud the fashion's new pursuit
of maxi, midi, and the trouser-suit,
Saving long legs from acrocyanosis,
Chilblains upon the thigh and vein thrombosis;
While find I comfort hearing from the wise:
"When hem-lines fall, stock-markets then do rise."

### SELF-EXPRESSION
*(after Patience Wrong)*

I SHOT an arrow in the air and pranged the Prossers' new *au pair*;
unerringly I aimed another, hit on her rump the deacon's mother; but no
one tells me to desist: the Min of Ed psychiatrist has said, "This child's not
bad nor stupid: she's acting out a role of Cupid."

### ON HIS TINNITUS

To one who has been long in city pent
And would from all oppressive noise be free,
The forest's stillness offers sanctuary:
The mountain peaks bestow a peace heaven-sent.
These havens once I sought; as well I spent
Days by a stream, remote in deep country,
Where less the play of angling was to me
Than finding in the quietness deep content.
Now silence have I none: sounds curious,
That have no source save cells in the cochlea,
Haunt my old ears in song continuous.
In cities now I stay; always I hear
The traffic's roar, canned music far and near:
The surging noises mask my tinnitus.

Erythroblast and normoblast,
Lymphocyte and monocyte,
What's the blood count? When's the meeting?
Are the monthly figures right?

"Cast your fly just farther out Sor,
By the sally bushes there;
You remember, last July Sor,
How you hooked the big one there."

Minute fragments for biopsy,
Twenty cells, not more I vow,
"Please exclude a carcinoma,"
Try a Papanicolaou!

"Will I get the rods out now Sor,
Lovely morning, fresh and cool;
Daybreak's just the time you know Sor,
For a salmon in the pool."

Myocardium rather flabby,
Coronaries calcified,
Marked fibrosis, much stenosis,
"Can't you tell us why he died?"

Kerry skies and Kerry waters,
Men with time enough to spare,
Time to talk and stop and listen,
Lord, I wish that I were there.
Peace that fills the wide horizons,
Lakes and hills; the picture's clear;
Shore and stream so well remembered
But – I'll not be there this year.

THOUGHTS FROM JUNG

Deep within the psyche are
Animus and anima.
Wraithlike, old, phylogenetic,
Ego all antipathetic,
Born to be the death of us,
Anima and animus.

## TOXIC SPRAYS

Once charlock in these cornfields was loud with honey-bees:
It made a Matisse picture – but it brought no subsidies;
To reap three tonnes an acre a Euro-farmer needs
Those gentlemen with face-masks on, there spraying pests and
   weeds:
Hormones for the bindweed,
Docks and marigolds,
DDT for aphids,
Copper for the moulds,
Carbamates for couch-grass, so deep its rhizomes lie;
Then hide your face, my darling, while the gentlemen come by!

### SEX AT ALTITUDE
*(prompted by a note in* The Lancet *in 1971)*

"Discussion, thought, and opportunity for expression of sex were remarkably absent at altitude. People began to notice what they had been missing only below 12 000 ft on the way home."

I never want to ever miss
The sweet rewards of nuptial bliss,
So I will do my level best
To never climb Mount Everest.

### ULTRAVIOLET RADIATION
*(prompted by 1987 report on skin cancer)*

Fear much more the heat o' the sun
Than the furious winter's rages:
Bared for the cosmetic tan
Saxon skin too early ages.
Golden lads and lasses must
No sunbathing zealot trust.

Fear unscreened fluorescent lighting
And home heliotherapy,
On a fair skin expediting
Wrinkling and age atrophy:
Golden lads must heed in youth
This, a portent of new growth.

## ON DISCARDING AN OLD FRIEND

You've served me well these twenty years
Since first with you I failed to hear
Those rhonchi, creps, and bubbling râles,
So crystal clear to all my pals;
When first I sat as locum tenens,
Confused as in delirium tremens,
You kept me chin-up and unbowed
When terrorstruck before the crowd;
What miracles of healing skill
By your sole aid upon the ill
I've wrought in Afric's tropic lands,
When fear kept naked hearts in bands;
To general practice then returning
Your curves again increased my learning,
For, faced with patients fully clothed,
Through collars I've reached lower lobes;
But now your rubber's worn and perished
And, though your company I've cherished,
The old must go and yield to new –
    So, gentle Stethoscope, Adieu!

### THE ANATOMY AND PHYSIOLOGY
### OF THE EMOTIONS

The monkey was wild, as macaque can be,
In his cage of iron bars,
And he chattered his rage incessantly
At the medical men who came to see
Emotion in captivity,
Yet bruited to the stars.

The psychiatrist passed him by one day,
And cast him a knowing look.
"This chap's emotions are all astray",
He said. "There's a diagram in Gray
Which ought to show us all the way."
And he opened the massive book.

"Here we go round the limbic lobe,
And there's the entorrhinal.
This vicious circle we must probe;
His rage goes round the limbic lobe.
We need not touch the pallid globe
Nor common pathways final."

*Students:* The limbic lobe, the limbic lobe,
            And convolutions gyral.
            His rage goes round the limbic lobe
            In an uninhibited spiral.

The surgeon did as he was bid,
Accompanied by his legions.
The monkey lay with face all hid,
While somebody prised off his lid,
And fingers delved down deeply mid
Those hippocampal regions.

The monkey is mild, as macaque is not,
And has no need of a cage.
His emotions blow neither cold nor hot,
No simian snarls, he's changed on the spot,
From social outcast to a genial clot,
And placid old age without rage.

PRESCRIBERS' NOTES

*"An advertisement is a rich man asking you to give him more
money" (G. K. Chesterton)*

The postman homeward plods his weary way,
   His shoulders lightened of his heavy load,
Thinking he ought to get a rise in pay
   With seven doctors on his daily road.

Pamphlets and pictures to ensnare the eye,
   Samples their young will eat and sicken, he hoped.
Blotted enow to suck the salt sea dry,
   Into the dustbin straight they go, unoped.

The PMG has heard his heartfelt cries,
   His wages raised, up must the postage go.
The cost is added to the products' price.
   The hopeful man thinks that will stem the flow.

But, when the State will pay, let money burn!
   We need not dam the ever-widening stream.
Yet animated bust and storied urn
   Whisper, the State is you and me – and him.

*Epitaph*

Full many a Flower is born to blush unseen
   And waste its sweetness in a bonfire's air.
Full many a View of Zermatt or the spleen
   The dark unfathom'd caves of ocean bear.

A practisour there was with penne in fyste,
He had four thousand pacions on his lyste
And doctored them right spedely; to each
He gave two minutes, cutting short their speche,
Writing them scripte in Latin most impure.
He had a verray pretty signature
Which none coude rede, but noöne ever tryed.
He had a motor carre in which to ryde
And eke a bagge to hold his stock-in-trade
– Divers certificates of every shade –
These he dispensed with a lavish grace,
Writing the details in the appropriate place.
With these and him his pacions were content,
He had no neede for any instrument.
He took no trouble, but he gave none
So he stood high with high-ups everyone,
Small wonder all came floccynge to his door
He was a parfit general practisour.

CORONARY

At first, unease,
As if the real things
Have no substance.
And then
Pain
Erupting
Like a flame
Seated in the mediastinal pit,
Which blazes up
Scorching, numbing
The molten centre of the world.
Now, stillness
Eyes closed, and a whisper,
"Is someone coming?"
"Yes, darling, keep still"
And there they are,
Strong men,
Blue-uniformed,
Competent.
"Hold this and breathe"

Oh! dousing ease.
Arms lifting,
Wheeling,
Cold air darkness.
Then a rushing
Rocketing, swinging,
Wheeling.
Swing doors
On the bed
As he is.
Hands gentle
Unbuttoning
And in the chest
The furnace glows
White-hot.
And at last
Memory recedes
In the blessed Nepenthe
Of heroin.

## WEEKEND TOOTHACHE
### *(after Walter de la Mare)*

"Is there anybody there?" said the Traveller
Knocking on the Casualty door;
Long hours for a dentist he'd sought, he said,
And relief for his aching jaw.
Came forth, his arms akimbo, a picket –
A porter – and thus he spake:
"We don't reckon toothache's an urgent case:
Emergencies is all we'll take."
And the Traveller smote the door even
Louder and lifted his head:
"Call this not a National Health hospital –
That turns away pain!" he said.
And he vowed that within the next hour
That to Europe for treatment he'd go:
Aye, they heard the roar of his Jaguar
As he sped on the road to Heathrow.

## DRUG INTERACTIONS . . .
### *(after Henry Reed's "Naming of parts . . .")*

Today we have naming of drugs. Last week,
We had the alteration of TB treatment in slow acetylators.
　　And next week
We shall have the eternal consequences of aspirin ingestion on the
　　stomach. But today,
Today we have naming of drugs. The stroke patient
Lies awkwardly positioned on his left side, staring blankly into
　　space,
　　And today we have naming of drugs.

This patient is on baclofen. He is more interestingly
On amiodarone, whose wide-ranging adverse effects you will see
As soon as you are qualified. And this is carbenoxolone,
Which in your case you should not prescribe. The nurse
Makes one of her tireless journeys with a bedpan.
　　Which in our case we should not prescribe.

This drug is a loop diuretic. In heart failure
It is often supplemented with inadequate potassium. Please do not
Use these supplementations in hypertension. These are purely
　　routine,
And in most cases unnecessary. The junior house officer
Is 'phoning the clinical chemist for results which are purely routine,
　　And in most cases unnecessary.

And this, as you know, is phenytoin, it works centrally by
Inhibiting abnormal electrical activity. It has to be monitored
   because
Of a narrow therapeutic window. This is so important that
Next term there will be lectures on it. Outside the ground frost is
   heavy,
Inhibiting activity. The sky reaches out a pale blue,
   Through the therapeutic window.

Through the therapeutic window, the castle stands,
Routine and unnecessary. The side effects of carbenoxolone appear
   bleak,
And the sun's diffuse rays shine weakly requiring supplementation
With potassium, which is so important that next term
There will be lectures on it. The overuse of digoxin appears green;
   For today we have naming of drugs.

TO A LEECH
*(Burns' "Immortal Memory" as seen after a 1986 article on
new uses for the leech)*

Wee, sleekit, starved, unlo'esome beastie,
That finds a mortal's blude sae tasty,
On this bruised tissue there's a feastie
To break thy fast;
Upon a surgeon's finger-plasty
This role thou hast.

For, Leechie, thou hast fibrinases
That digest clots in vein thromboses:
Thou canst prevent capillary stasis
Wi' thy saliva.
For grafted limbs, facing necrosis,
Thou art the saviour.

ALLERGY IN A COUNTRY CHURCHYARD

The sexton has not tolled the bell today:
He has a disability award –
His lungs fibrosed from handling mouldy hay,
Affirm the Pneumoconiosis Board.

The anthem solo is no longer sung;
Faint rise the hymns from the depleted choir:
Too breathless now with mushroom-pickers' lung
Is he whose tenor voice we did admire.

Brief is the sermon of the rural dean,
Nasal his voice in the Magnificat:
Endure he must with antihistamine
Hay fever hazards of his habitat.

For soaking rain, the parson's supplication,
That pollen be not wind-borne from the flora:
For summer sunshine, pray the congregation,
And hay preserved from micropolyspora.

A PLAQUE UNVEILED

A crowd there was in Ramsgate Town
To honour Dr Collis Browne,
Whose Chlorodyne's saved countless chaps
From having untoward mishaps.
And many another skilled invention
He made, too numerous to mention.
So Collis Browne deserves his plaque
Which mayor, mayoress, and town clerk
With friends and kinsmen by the score
(Although he died in 'eighty-four)
Unveiled, and thus gave him his meed
Which he (or she) who runs may read.

LAMENT . . .
*(on a period of inertia IEN)*

'twas nice once to read *The Lancet*, when tired
    of deaths and disorders inborn or acquired,
of outbreaks of plague in whole populations,
    of viruses, blood-pressure, and operations.

There used to be items inciting to laughter,
    allowing to go on with cancers thereafter.

Why has this refreshing source of hilarity
    shrunken to present regrettable rarity?

Have all your former peripatetics
    turned into listless hypokinetics?

Your budding Betjeman's lament
   in issue August 12 (now lent
to others seeking erudition)
   may be fair comment on the sad condition

Of some late issues (be they few, admitted)
   from which "In England Now" has been *omitted.*

In other weeks, a column-inch suffices
   to take the weary mind off haemolysis,

Blood-lead in taxi-drivers, crises ante partum,
   cyclic AMP, *Diphyllobothrium latum.*

Peripatetics of the world unite –
   you have nothing to lose but your copyright!

### THE REGISTRAR'S LOVE-SONG
*(after the poet shown acrostically)*

Joan, Joan Hunter Dunn, Nurse J. Hunter Dunn,
Of my thinning hair you are apt to make fun;
Have you never heard of the saying, my sweet:
No grass grew for long on an occupied street.

Baldheadedness favours the young candidate,
Exalts his importance; and haply his fate
To be a consultant e're he's thirty-one:
Just deserts for baldies, Nurse J. Hunter Dunn!

Endocrines in their make-up are stated to spur
Masculinity strong in most men with no hair:
Aim not at the hirsute, if you would have fun,
Nor disdain this Kojak, Nurse Joan Hunter Dunn.

### A PLACE OF STRIFE

O, Mr Porter, what shall I do?
They've put me in this private ward and nobody asked you.
Maybe you frown on BUPA and doctors' private fees
But won't you wheel me to the X-ray, Mr Porter, please?

Here comes the radiologist: it's nearly ten o'clock;
He's had to park his Bentley by the distant laundry block.
Consultants are no longer reserved a parking space:
The union-harassed management dare not allot a place.

You trundle by my doorway with studied unconcern
The patients from the main ward: I guess I've missed my turn.
No go my private side-ward, my Private Patients' Plan!
O, Mr Porter, what a silly girl I am!

### PRONOUNCING PUZZLE PIECE FOR POETIC PLUMBERS

THE other day I was meditating on the strange difficulties posed by the words reād and reăd. As a child I had great faith in Huntley and Palmers' Reading biscuits as an aid to overcoming illiteracy and found it said when I learned that Reading described their birthplace rather than their effects. A similar problem affects electricians. Who knows how many deaths may occur every year from confusion over the earthing of a point by a lead-covered lead, which, having lead over the leads, leads to a lead pipe? The possible hazards for plumbers can be best revealed thus:

> The news of plastic pipes I read
> Confirms the views of books I read
> Which says their increased use will lead
> To far less poisoning from lead.

# XI

# Special Occasions

THERE are some laws, known to us all, which are never codified. The post-office queue, for example, which stops as soon as you join it; the urgent report which goes missing only to reappear mysteriously ten days later; the telephone that stops ringing just as one is about to pick it up; and, from the patient's point of view, the happy band of nurses who are there when he is laughing but are nowhere to be found when a bedpan is frantically needed.

It all relates to Murphy's law. This states that in any given situation, anything which can go wrong will go wrong. And to Corrigan's corollary which comments that Murphy was an optimist. This is well known to those of us who have to show important people round our hospitals. I once took a bishop to a long-stay psychiatric unit. In response to his kindly offer of a toffee, one of the patients told him explicitly what he should do with it. Even an immediate glass of medicinal sherry failed to revive the learned prelate entirely.

I was reminded of the no doubt apocryphal story of the visit of a prominent politician to the same institution. Towards the end of his tour, he thought to address a few words to the patients. When he finished a voice from the back of the hall yelled "Rubbish!" He was not soothed by the remark of the nurse in charge who said it was the first rational statement she had heard the patient make in the past five years.

REUNIONS are notoriously traumatic and the 40th anniversary dinner of our medical year was no exception. I recognised one man who had kept his chubby face as well as his hair; and another who had managed to retain his short-back-and-sides. But all the rest were spectres who loomed unknown from the past – mainly because a modicum of back-and-sides was all that was left to them. "Now who can this be?" The replies disclosed more than the faces: the voice, the mannerisms had changed less than the appearance. The characters remained true to form. The beavers were more pointedly eager, the wide boys wider in more senses than one. The funny man was still telling stories, the ascetic had spent his life in Africa. It all produced an uncanny sensation, almost as though the 40 years had gone by while you looked away and back again. Everyone looked different, yet they were just the same people.

I HAVE just entered my 50th year as a doctor. As a result all the doubts I have had in the past regarding jubilees and centenaries have been revived. The Festival of Britain, intended to indicate the half-way mark of the 20th century, generated a considerable correspondence in *The Times*. The point at issue was whether the Festival should take place at the beginning of the year 1950 or at its end – whether the triumph was to have *reached* the 50th year or to have *completed* it without disaster. Inevitably this led to an argument about whether the century should be considered to have begun on Jan 1, 1900, or Jan 1, 1901, and this rather red herring shifted the debate to the date of the birth of Christ, a subject which I have no intention of bringing up here.

On the whole I still favour the school of thought which rested its case on the fact that no batsman is applauded for making a century until he has completed his hundredth run, and on this basis I ought not to celebrate my fifty until a year's time. This would be in line with the fears of my mother, a staunch Presbyterian, who would never allow me to have my birthday party even a day ahead, even if it was administratively highly desirable to do so. Her reason was that I might be struck down by a vengeful Jehovah for her arrogance in assuming that I would survive until the correct date.

THIS was definitely his last year he had decided. It wasn't just the exercise, it was the time of year. He should have guessed when the advertisement had said "seasonal work". His chest always played him up in the cold weather. He stopped, one foot wedged in the guttering, half leaning, half sitting on the steeply pitched slates. What a winter it had been. Snow was swirling down between the buildings and already lying thickly on the ground. "It may all look like a Dutch 'winter scene' Christmas card – but it doesn't make my job any easier." It wasn't even just the weather he was bitter about. People don't bother about their roofs or chimneys any more. Loose slates, insecure guttering, dirty blocked chimneys; he couldn't remember the last time he had a "clear run". He clambered upwards, doing his best to compensate for the slippiness of the slates by quickening his stride. Chimney stack, London brick, some superficial weathering, but generally good condition, about 1910 he reckoned. It looked safe enough. There's a thought, no wonder his insurance company had played merry hell this year, what with his chest and the increased number of claims. His wife had even got in on the act, insisting that he wear this ridiculous orange harness. He clipped the central ring of this to a rope secured around the base of the chimney. Reaching up he got a good first hold, despite a loose brick sliding down the roof, bouncing over the gutter and arcing out of sight. With a final heave he rose and stood astride the chimney pots – two, Victorian, and both cracked. He slipped a small tablet under his tongue, more as a reward than to ease his increasing chest tightness. "Sod tradition," he said out loud, dropping a gaudily wrapped parcel into the nearer of the two chimney pots.

MATRON vouches for the truth of this one, for it happened to a friend of hers. This friend had two engagements one afternoon – a funeral and a more genial encounter at a tea-party. She put on a sober black hat, intending to change it after the funeral for her new "this season's flowery creation", which she carefully laid on the back seat of her Austin Seven. At the graveside she could not forbear when it was all over to look around at the wreaths and their inscriptions. Suddenly she saw her own new hat among them; one of the undertaker's men had seen it left behind in the car, and had tried to be helpful.

"I am a bit nervous," I said. "Don't worry," said the interviewer. "It will be all right. Trust me." "Sixty seconds!" called an anonymous voice. "What will you ask?" I inquired. "Oh, the usual questions." "Forty seconds!" "How you had an excellent university career." "Thirty seconds!" "Then after graduating and Army service, you decided to specialise." "Twenty seconds!" "How you thought the greatest challenge of the age was geriatrics." "Ten seconds!" "And how you decided to devote your life to the care of the elderly." "Now!" "Tell me, doctor," said the TV lady, "isn't it true that you regard old people as third-class citizens, a drain on health resources, and in many cases, not even worth keeping alive? Have you no conscience at all?" "Eh!" I exclaimed.

# XII

# Fauna and Flora

I WAS being shown round a patient's well-kept garden by his wife last summer when we came on some cucumbers of unsurpassed magnificence. My praise fell on stony ground. "I wouldn't touch them," said my guide, "I don't like the way they are grown – terribly unhygienic." Something warned me not to probe further.

My own attempts at cucumber growing having always been a dismal failure, I cross-examined the gardener two days later. After extravagant appreciation of his horticultural efforts I delicately approached the subject of the cucumbers. He shifted uneasily from one foot to the other and I judged that the moment had now come for a little mild corruption, and he pocketed my coin with evident satisfaction. "You won't tell Johnstone?" he anxiously inquired. (Johnstone being the proprietor of a local hotel, to whom I suspect he sells the cucumbers.) I had promised to be discreet. "I wouldn't mention this to just anybody, but you being a doctor will understand. The truth is there's nothing like mare's piss for watering them cucumbers, especially if she's near term. Farmer Smith's lass saves it for me – she's a married woman or I wouldn't have asked her."

Mentioning this later to a well-known obstetrician I found him unimpressed – he lives in a flat and takes but a languid interest in gardens – but he told me that the growth-stimulating properties of pregnant urine were familiar to the ancient Egyptians. A papyrus over 3000 years old contains the following instructions. "Let the woman take a pinch of corn and a handful of good earth and mix them in a shallow vessel. Each morning she must pass a little urine into the vessel. If the corn sprouts she is surely pregnant."

ONE dark rainy night our good friend Walter was called out to see a woman with suspected cholecystitis. Arriving at the house he was greeted by a large and enthusiastic dog, who rose from a puddle to spatter mud, water, and hair all over W. Door opened in response to frantic knocking. Dog bounded upstairs and leaped on patient's bed – transferring more mud, hair, to patient. Examination was difficult with dog sprawled over patient's abdomen. Finally, in exasperation, W said, "Would you mind terribly if we asked your dog to wait outside?" "*My* dog," groaned the patient, "I thought it was *your* dog!"

OUR elderly cat had the characteristic multiple pathology of the declining, so I asked for a vet to call when one of them was out our way. The senior partner honoured us with a personal visit. A good psychologist, he sat on the sofa and just watched his patient for a long time before he examined her. "Well," he summed up, "she's senile and blind and has pretty bad chronic bronchitis. And arthritis, and very likely other things as well. But I notice she still purrs. There are two possible approaches. One is to do nothing. The other is to give her a course of injections to improve her bronchitis, though it would probably be back to square one within a week." He paused and waited for my reaction. "The first choice seems kinder," I said. He was delighted. "Good! Let her live out her diminished life in peace. She is adjusting to her disabilities. Any treatment would have been – as is usual in such cases – more for the sake of the owner's conscience than for the animal." I realise the parallel is imperfect, but I have been wondering how often elderly human beings are subjected to treatment that is really to satisfy the relatives.

I NOW have no doubt that a country cottage is the best antidote to a consultant's life in a large industrial city. Stepping over the threshold seems to induce relaxation.

It isn't like the Ritz; indeed the farmworker whose it was viewed it as unfit for human habitation. It is timbered, black and white, and built about 1640. So far only one thing has marred it. The mental tranquillity of the Sunday has sometimes been replaced on the Monday morning, during outpatients, by a humiliating looseness of the bowels.

I had thought of consulting a psychiatrist, as it seemed an obvious escape mechanism, symbolising an unconscious desire to rid myself of the humdrum of routine work. But serious consideration will now have to be given to an alternative diagnosis. I've just discovered that there is a dead horse in our water-supply.

I BOUGHT such a nice, friendly, healthy, and inexpensive, canary from one of our larger stores recently. Three days later he died. I contacted the pets department and told them of my sad loss. In view of the sudden demise I rightly claimed another bird. I wrapped him tenderly and returned him. A few days later he came back stuffed. Enclosed was a bill for £25.

IT was an emergency all right, and I just happened to be around. The patient was an elderly, rather prickly male, and he had walked straight into, and then managed to get himself twisted up in, some cricket netting set up on his own back lawn for the children to play in. It was wrapped tightly round his head and neck, and round one leg; and, apparently after some struggling with it, he had gone into a state of hysterical stupor. That was how I found him. He lay there on the lawn, curled up in a state of intense flexor spasm, just breathing, unable to speak, incontinent of faeces. He had such a tight grip on the netting I couldn't begin to get it away from him.

I don't know what his poor wife must have thought, but I do know what I thought: that this was no time for unheroic measures. Strangulation was one danger, death from sheer terror or exhaustion another. I happened to have a little chloroform handy (but no other anaesthetic), and in no time at all I was administering chloroform to a patient for the first time in twenty years. He was soon under, and once the spasm had gone I got the netting off him easily enough. Then suddenly, of course, his breathing had to stop. I thought of the kiss of life, but his little old wrinkled face put me off, so I compromised with squeezing his chest a few times and fortunately this started spontaneous respiration again.

He didn't come round properly for some little time, and I began to wonder if my massive and inexpert administration of chloroform had not hit his liver – perhaps not inappropriately – for six. However, some ten minutes after I stopped the anaesthetic he was on his feet, and five minutes later he was walking. He didn't thank me, he didn't say a word. I doubt if he was grateful. And I don't suppose I shall ever set eyes on that patient again. He was, you see, a hedgehog.

COURAGE, audacity, and gentleness; these are just a few of the attributes required for that great field-sport – picking blackberries. Above all is its motivation – search for perfection. If you are not a perfectionist, if you are simply one of those prepared only to fill your basket to the brim, if you sink to accepting the small, the hard, and those not wholly black, then you will make no demand upon virtue. Nor will you develop the spotter's skill, that sense for the trail which will lead you to the perfect fruit. You won't even have discovered the rule of all great blackberriers: the finest fruit lies hidden behind a leaf, coyly shielding its beauty.

To catch your quarry you must first choose your equipment with care – none of those thin plastic bags which will be torn by the first advance into a thicket. And beware of the paper carrier-bag; it may look stout enough, but as the bottom becomes damp the weight of the fruit above will surely break through at the crucial moment as you stumble on the difficult homeward path. If it is to be a basket, it must be stable both on the ground and balanced on a platform of briars. With it, a crooked walking-stick, not only to draw the distant branch into your loving grasp, but to serve as a probe to find level ground as you advance forwards through the thickets. The professional makes a reconnaissance over likely ground; not for him the obvious fruit at the roadside or beside the path. He knows that there is always better beyond the first encounter; the chase leads ever on, for the body must be thrust ever harder against unyielding thorns, although the foot may slip, endangering the body and spilling the precious catch. Behind the finest pick is always the risk of loss of all, for alongside must lie the basket resting ready to receive, but prone to fall, while one hand pulls the briar forward and the other hand plucks the prize.

*Ah, but whose other hand?*
THE battle had been going on for some time with neither side gaining the advantage. Occasionally our sticks clashed as we reached at full stretch for a better grip. From my unseen opponent and me came no sound save the grunts of our exertions. Then suddenly things went my way; one last desperate thrust and heave and the prize was mine. With a crow of triumph I tore at it with hands already dripping purple-red. From my adversary not a word. Then, as I looked about me for new peaks to conquer came a voice, muffled and reproachful. "What blackberry pickers need", it said "is a code of ethics."

I AM generally known in the district, not as a doctor, but as the owner of Conky, an English setter. On Nov 5, although kept indoors, Conky was profoundly disturbed by fireworks. The following morning a car backfired and this was probably the reason for the trouble. That afternoon he had to be left in the house alone for a short time and now was profoundly anxious through having misunderstood the nature of the explosions. Accordingly, he prepared for a siege. Down at the back of the cushions of my armchair he buried two jam tarts and, so far as is practicable, half a pound of butter. He is an intelligent dog and, as is usual in the neurotic, he has good insight: with the jam tarts and butter he buried *A Short Textbook of Psychiatry*.

THE gymkhana in aid of the General Practitioner Accident Service was in full swing. Little heels prodded viciously at recalcitrant flanks, fences collapsed, judges solemnly conferred, and equine ears sported rosettes in red, white, and blue. Children howled, got lost, fell into ditches, or got covered all over in something sticky.

It was a very hot day. The Medical Officer, the brains of the whole effort, sat exhausted at the door of his tent behind a can of warm beer and tried to calculate whether the takings would run to a radio-telephone or merely a dozen drip-sets. His eyelids drooped, he repeatedly forgot the running total and had to start all over again. He lashed out with his programme at a drunken wasp sampling his beer, but missed. It was a very hot day.

Suddenly the Tannoy whistled, crackled, and spoke. "The doctor is wanted very urgently in the judge's enclosure." The doctor came to instantly, and almost choked on the aluminium ring of his beer can. Then, recollecting that these are now valuable, he retrieved it and added it carefully to the takings in the cash box. Picking up his little black bag, he rushed off to the emergency.

A crowd surrounded a barely visible body on the ground. He was met by Colonel Z, the senior judge. "It's my Labrador," he said. "You must do something. She's been the family pet for nine years and I couldn't go home if she doesn't . . ." The dog lay on the ground, breathing laboriously, a pink froth growing round its mouth, its eyes already glazed. You could not really say that it was on its last legs, because all four legs pointed heavenwards, rather like a Thurber drawing. After a brief examination, our doctor, whose knowledge of canine ills was non-existent, diagnosed pulmonary oedema. Without much hope, and without any idea of the right dosage, he administered an intravenous injection of frusemide, and followed with a shot of aminophylline. For a while, nothing happened. Then, to his amazement, the animal stood up, wagged his tail, and relieved itself at some length, or rather volume, over its master's highly polished riding boots.

Just then the vet arrived. The colonel welcomed him. The vet inspected the patient, made a few doggy noises, and raised an eyelid (the dog's, not his own) the way vets do. "She'll be all right" he said. The colonel shook him warmly by the hand, thanked him profusely, patted him on the shoulder, questioned how they could ever manage without him, and, as he left, reminded him to send his fee.

This was too much for the Medical Officer, now on his knees repacking his bag. "What about thanking me?" he inquired. "What has *he* done for the dog? I treated it, he's done nothing. And what about *my* fee, and the cost of the drugs I've used?' The vet assumed a curious expression which attempted to avoid looking smug and embarrassed simultaneously. The colonel's lip curled slightly. "I understood you are in the Health Service," he said.

WHEN I visited the Hubbards I could never understand why their dog was hustled into the back-kitchen. I never heard it bark nor look in the least aggressive. It was a borzoi, finely groomed, very long in the nose, and it always looked unspeakably bored. Usually when I knocked I heard a scuffle while Mike was being dragged with skidding paws along the narrow hall to the back of the house. But last Monday when I knocked I heard Mike sniffing diagnostically on the other side. I inferred that the family was out and that Mr Hubbard was either too deaf to hear my knock or too immobilised by his lumbago to come to the door. Accordingly I walked straight in. As I anticipated, the dog came up to me and was perfectly friendly. I pride myself that I understand dogs and that this sympathy is reciprocated.

I walked along the dark hall to the kitchen where Mr Hubbard was bending over the table holding his back with both hands. At that moment I felt a sudden tug on my coat. Mike had taken a grip on it. "I say, call your dog off Mr Hubbard, it's got hold of my coat!"

"I can almost touch my toes," said Mr Hubbard, bending with a conspicuous lack of confidence towards the floor. Mike released his grip on my coat, opened his jaws and sank his teeth into my hamstrings. This was very painful. "Hubbard!" I screamed, "Call this cursed bloodhound away, it's got hold of my leg!" Mr Hubbard was, unhappily, fixed in flexion. In this position he advanced towards us, clicking his tongue in mild abuse. "Tch tch, come away, come away, now, boy; it's only the doctor."

SOME days ago I embarked for the UK, home and penury, and settled down to a few weeks' comfortable respite before house and work hunting engulfed me. But I began to itch. Now a little itch here and there is nothing among friends in the tropics, but this one not only affected the most inconvenient parts but also worked itself up into veritable paroxysms every night. "Much as these symptoms would suggest scabies in any of your other patients," I explained to the regimental medical officer "you will realise, I am sure, that this cannot be my case." "Obviously, Sir, those little creatures could not be the cause," he replied, knowing instinctively that senior officers simply do not have scabies, "but I suggest that you try a routine treatment or two with benzoate, just in case there might be some parasitic background to your complaint." He handed me a bottle of emulsion and I retired to the bathroom with grace and a secret determination that no promotion ever come the way of that young doctor. Reader, between ourselves, the relief after but a few hours was truly and absolutely incredible. I can imagine no greater boon to poor itching humanity, and most strongly recommend you to try it yourself.

WE yield to none in our affection for the bright-eyed creatures of the woodland, even though they're a bunch of free-loaders who've left our garden without bud or berry. Our quarrel is with the mole, thanks to whom the lawn resembles the sort of terrain portrayed on a picture-postcard sent home to Mum by a lunar astronaut.

The Ministry of Agriculture expert was a dreamy little bald-headed chap who made arch references to "the little gentleman in grey velvet". He gave us an illustrated booklet all about moles which said the mole's nom de guerre was *Talpa europaea* and that he, or she, had 44 teeth and was never found in Ireland. We now know it would have saved us trouble if we'd just shipped our lawn across there, but as it was we simply followed the book. We set traps and put liquid paraffin and mothballs down the runs. These ensured that our moles were regular in their habits and that their little grey velvet coats were free from moths. We also sat for two sodden hours in a deckchair watching the latest molehill. We had a shotgun because the booklet advised that any molish activity be rewarded with both barrels. Down in the molehill nothing stirred, but when we were lifted out of the chair, there was a new molehill underneath it.

In despair we again telephoned the Ministry of Agriculture man. He suggested putting carbide down the runs "and waiting for rain". All last week you could hardly go out except by boat, but we spent the morning carbiding the runs. When we'd finished, the sun came out and we had to go round again with a watering-can. There was a frightful smell of acetylene gas, and in defence we lit a cigarette and flicked away the match. With a series of rumbling explosions, the entire lawn lifted six inches, disintegrated, and fell back again, mostly upside down. The bright-eyed creatures of the woodland took off in all directions, the greenhouse roof fell in, and the seismograph at Kew blew a fuse. We've had no moles since. Neither have we had a lawn.

*Help was at hand, for two weeks later came the following prescription:*

DOWN here in the Andredsweald we know a thing or two about *Talpa europaea*. "Moles," said Old Nin, brushing the froth off his whiskers in the Stone Quarry Inn, "oi 'ates 'em. But," he added craftily, "oi now knows 'ow to fox 'em." He, too, had consulted the Min of Ag about his lawn and a man had come all the way to Chelwood Gate – very likely the same chap we read about in this column a fortnight ago. In addition to buckshot, mothballs, and acetylene gas he had recommended strychnine. You first catch some worms and next place them in a box containing the correct admixture of strychnine and earth. Surprisingly the worms don't seem to mind eating this, and after some time (and preferably when the moon is gibbous) you shove them down the moles' holes. The moles then remark, like Luther after the Diet of Worms, "we can take no other course" and gently expire. Well, that's the theory, but Old Nin felt a bit anxious about the possibility of the strychnine getting in his soup. Providentially he read, about this time, a letter in *Country Life* (or was it *The Field*?). Planted at strategic points around the periphery of his lawn, Old Nin soon had any number of the seedlings of *Capparis spinosa* holding their handsome little heads aloft. No more moles. Honest.

*Guess who had the last laugh:*
IT is always difficult to admit defeat, to confess error. Yet my scientific training, my very Oath even, compels honesty, and the truth is that *Capparis spinosa* has bowed down before the hordes of *Talpa*. Alas, I now hear from Old Nin that his clinical trial, double-blind in a sense, has "resulted in a crushing victory for the moles". Can they, he asks, develop an immunity to, or worse, a taste for capers? Meanwhile it is back to tradition. The voice of the mole-catcher will be heard in the land.

I HAVE a friend who is a zoologist. One of his responsibilities is to build up the definitive collection of skeletons for his department, a task in which he is very assiduous. He collects any dead creature he finds. He has people acting as agents all over the world, so that parcels of various sizes and odours arrive for him at work. When he hears of a new specimen, all else goes from his mind and time is forgotten. He is also known to dig up long-buried farm animals especially if they happen to be of breeds now very rare, though he has been less keen on this since the time he excavated the skeletons of four cows buried sixty years ago. He asked the farmer whether he knew what they had died of. "Oh yes, it was anthrax." The public health people got quite upset about it all, I gather.

When I met him the other day, he was looking very angry. Apparently he had had a message from a Scandinavian contact announcing that he had obtained the corpses of two reindeer and he was arranging for them to be flown to England forthwith; could my friend find out what time the flight would arrive and pick them up? Excited, he phoned the airport, and told them he was expecting a couple of reindeer that night. Then, to his surprise and anger, he had been treated most rudely. The man on the other end of the line had told him, before slamming down the receiver, that he was very busy, he was sick to death of practical jokers, and would my friend be kind enough to go away – or words to that effect. Why were they so rude, he complained, in the face of a perfectly civil inquiry? I gently pointed out that it had been Christmas Eve.

THE National Press has had a lot to say about London's "supermice". These intrepid creatures, resistant to all lawful poisons, increase and multiply in the comfort of our centrally heated homes, cosseted by soft insulating material. Their favourite foods are the two permitted poisons: chloralose, which gives them good restful sleep, and warfarin, which helps their blood to whip round their fit little bodies. Sleek and muscular, they are getting stronger and cleverer than mice have ever been before.

Some of the best of this lot have been resident in my house for too long, frightening the cat and so on. They'd be there yet if it weren't for a strange occurrence which makes one mindful of the empiricism of medicine. It makes one think of Alexander Fleming rummaging in his desk for his mouldy sandwich or Horace Wells in fits of gassy laughter because his tooth had just been yanked out. Late the other night I heard a tiny throat being cleared in a peremptory manner. Two mice were looking mean-ingfully at the warfarin canister. A glance in the corners told me why. They'd eaten all the bait I'd put down, they were peckish, and they wanted service. I suppose if anything had been left in the can I would have given it to them. I always have done before: I don't like scenes. But it was empty, so I chucked it in the bin, retreated to bed, and left the mice grizzling among themselves. A couple of days passed, and we seemed to be seeing a bit less of them. Then one turned up in the kitchen, but he seemed slowed up somehow, and paused from time to time as he crossed the floor. Another started up a table leg, but he packed it in halfway up and slithered to the bottom, front paws pressing his sternum. Thereafter every day brought a corpse or two, still sleek and well-nourished, but unaccountably dead. Not being one of your FRCPs it took me a lot of thought to arrive at the diagnosis, but at last I had it. Not only were they warfarin-*resistant*, they were also warfarin-*dependent*. To me had been vouchsafed the answer to London's supermice: take away their warfarin and give them coronaries.

LIFE in most hospitals passes quietly, and any minor departure from routine, such as the ejection of the residents' piano from an upstairs window, is liable to hit newspaper headlines. Our latest claim to fame began with night sister's discovery of an unwanted man in the sluice. For reasons still not clear, the resident obstetric officer was summoned to deal with her attendant vasomotor phenomena, and, since resident obstetri-cians tend to spring from a small-statured race, our colleague saw fit to bear a long stretcher-pole under his arm for protection. Meanwhile the intruder had vanished without trace and the police decided to bring their blood-hound into action. A large, sad-faced animal called Pluto was duly brought to the scene of the incident; but, overwhelmed by a host of new smells, he shook himself violently, chased his tail a few times, and made off in the direction of the labour ward where he barked loudly at a placenta lying in a bowl. The commotion woke the babies in the nursery, who all started yelling at once. Pluto took to instant flight and, after a careful search, was discovered ten minutes later in the grounds, digging a hole. The sergeant who had long since despaired of finding the right scent, then announced that he would take the dog for one last frisk before retiring to the station. This was a good cue for making some tea; and, with Pluto contentedly munching an underdone sausage from the night-nurses' supper, a good time was had by all.

# XIII

# Children

I HAD just excised a cyst from the buttock of the deputy chairman of the parks and cemeteries committee and was still caparisoned in cap, mask, gown, gloves, and white rubber bootees when I strode into the female ward for chronic dermatoses. The piano was open and prompted by an unpredictable whim, I sat down at it. There was a flutter of excitement among the patients. "The doctor's going to play!" Those who were not confined to bed gathered round. In a bed next the piano slept a pale schoolgirl with severe acne. Better, I reflected, be awakened by Bach than by anyone. So I began the *First Prelude* (Book 1): over twenty years of practice I have been able to commit only two things to memory and this was one of them. I could see that it was going down well, so before the last chord had had time to take a good grip of the strings I started *Finlandia*, which was my other tune. At the end there was such sincere and heart-warming applause and cries of "Encore" that I was emboldened to take off my surgical gloves. I played *Finlandia* again.

Through a receding tide of smiling and admiring females I made my way towards the door with my head slightly bent forward in an attitude that cannot be adopted with safety by any but the most profoundly modest. If there was something that unsettled me, something that may have robbed the occasion of the full sweetness of success it was that the acne child seemed to be still asleep. And I had opened the piano top.

I got back to the theatre flushed but happy and began the next case. I was in the middle of this when I heard the radio in the ward playing the *Study in C minor* (No 12, Opus 10). This is, of course, the pianist's Parnassus. It should be attempted only by the great. As I said to nurse, "Women are simply incapable of playing this study: they have neither the wrist-power nor the emotional reserves to sustain it." As if possessed by a power higher than myself I got up from the theatre-table and walked in a kind of somnambulistic trance towards the ward door. I was not unconscious that nurse was watching me with a strange mixture of embarrassment, confusion, and unbridled admiration. How could she know how deeply I was moved? The hospital secretary popped his head round the corner.

"Might be Backhaus," I said.

"Back where?" he asked.

"Or Iso Elinson."

"Is who what?"

"No Claudio Arrau. That incisive touch! I would know it anywhere . . . What magical male incisiveness! What technical supremacy . . . perhaps lacking that full-blooded passion of Elinson . . . but brilliant all the same . . ."

I opened the door so that we could all hear a little better. The acne child was seated at the piano.

THE reportedly very backward 5-year-old seemed the ideal case to start the new combined round of child psychiatrist and paediatrician. He did not seem to be all that stupid, provided he had plenty of time and was not asked several more questions while he was thinking out the first. To give him time, the kind lady handed him a pencil and paper and asked him to draw something. Very slowly he produced a recognisable car and then adorned its top with two small spheres with a tall straight structure standing between them. When he was asked the meaning of this obvious symbolism, he turned very slowly to the psychiatrist and croaked: "It's a police car, you dope."

THE local infants-class teacher has been trying to select the angel for this year's nativity play. Among fifteen little girls, all potential angels, the position is as follows: No 1 "don't want to"; No 2 doesn't speak English; No 3 scarcely speaks anything; No 4 is garrulous, and no-one could hope to hear the rest of the cast; No 5 is unreliably continent; No 6 has a spotty face; No 7 has a sore nose and running ears; Nos 8 and 9 are very irregular attenders and no understudy is planned; No 10 is naughty (pinches the other children); No 11 was the angel last Christmas; No 12 has bright blue tights and won't be parted from them under any consideration. All have been extremely ingratiating, providing teacher with various "delights", and pressing their claims with great frankness and no modesty.

But today measles claimed No 13 and No 14 is away with a cough. So the issue has more or less resolved itself, and this year's angel will be No 15.

Emma, aged 5, loved her greatgrandfather in that somewhat detached way that carries across four generations. The time came for her mother to break the news: "'Parky' has died, Emma." "Oh. Who told you?" "Your grandmother, darling." A pause; no tears; just indignation. "You shouldn't have listened!"

Johnnie, aged 8½, is the oldest inhabitant of our children's ward. When he was a few months old, his mother left him on the steps of a residential nursery. A few months later he contracted pneumonia. He has also overcome measles, chickenpox, mumps, and whooping-cough, all contracted in the ward. He has no mentality; he makes no purposive movement (save opening his mouth); he cannot see; it is doubtful whether he hears.

For many years Johnnie had no visitor. But about a year ago, the bed next to him was occupied by a boy about his own age who was in for some minor orthopaedic business. His mother came regularly and soon noticed that nobody ever came to visit the boy in the corner. So the next time she came, she brought a little toy for Johnnie; and for the rest of her son's stay she made a point, every day, of saying a few words to him and stroking his hair for a minute or so.

Her own boy is long out of the hospital, but she comes on most Sundays to the bed in the corner, and rarely empty-handed: a small toy, a piece of chocolate. Johnnie cannot see the toy, cannot understand – even if he hears – her words, and we shall never know if he enjoys chocolate. Her visits probably mean nothing to him; but I am sure they are not wasted, and that everybody in the ward is a kinder and nicer person as a result.

I HAD to spend some time comforting the distraught mother whose child was thought to be a behaviour problem. She had just taken him to a psychiatrist who among many searching questions had asked the 5-year-old: "If your sister is a girl, what is your brother?" No answer was forthcoming, and no doubt the appropriate score went down on the questionnaire. The mother came away somewhat bewildered.

To test my own 4-year-old daughter's reaction, I asked her: "If your sister is a girl, what is your brother?" A long pause followed, and then she said tartly: "A mouse." I said rather disappointedly, "Why did you say that?" The prompt reply was "Ask a silly question and you get a silly answer."

I was brought up in a part of Wales where aitch-dropping is endemic. At school, morning and evening, 150 of us assembled in the playground and chanted the Lord's Prayer "Our Father who art in Eaven, Alwyd be Thy Name." For years I sheltered under a beautiful umbrella in the certain knowledge that God was a Welshman. No wonder we so persistently won rugby's Triple Crown. For a time I went a little further and believed that the Trinity consisted of Alwyd, God, and Lloyd George. The other day a colleague and I were discussing the mistakes made by children in the meaning and interpretation of words, and I told him about Alwyd. In return he related how his 4½-year-old had tackled his first-ever homework. Father was reading the newspaper and small boy was working aloud: "One and one, son of a bitch is two, one and two, son of a bitch is three." My friend dropped his newspaper and asked for an explanation. "That's the way they teach us, Daddy." The following day father interviewed the headmistress and got the facts: "one and one the sum of which is two."

Personally I prefer Alwyd and son of a bitch.

How do you advise a girl who is besotted with animals and wants to spend her life working with them? She is not afraid of blood and guts, but veterinary medicine is out – she lacks the academic ability even for human medicine. One such was persuaded to pay a pound and feed her details into the careers computer. The answer? Butcher.

The whole family came along to outpatients – father, mother, and two girls aged 6 and 9. The complaint was that the girls couldn't sleep at night. They refused to go to bed until their parents did, insisted on the door between the children's and parents' bedrooms being left open all night, and had reduced mother and father to near hysteria. The suffering parents had obviously read some books on child psychology warning them of the dangers of repressing their children; I wish the author could have seen them.

I tried to point out that children need parents who are not afraid to tell them when to stop; that no child can cope with the idea that it is all-powerful, or the thought that no-one can restrain its most arrogant demands, &c, &c. Everyone departed looking thoughtful. I think the idea must have caught on because mother came back next week to report that the results of treatment had been dramatic. That same evening an enraged father had gone into the children's room and told them to go to sleep at once on pain of a sound thrashing, and had left the room slamming the communicating door. Both children had promptly fallen fast asleep while father lay awake all night with a violent headache.

Jimmy was seven years old and had leukaemia. Christmas was near when his mother and father learned the truth. This was in the days before chemotherapy had its now established place, and the tragedy of medicine lay bare: neither compassion nor the faintest glimmer of a last hope could soften the cold truth. "We can do nothing. A few weeks, perhaps; that's all; nothing more. Only a miracle could –"

With treatment, Jimmy gradually improved. On Christmas Day, he sat up in bed surrounded by toys and sweets, and his face shone with soap, joy, and cortisone. Soon his blood was normal and his marrow too; his spleen could no longer be felt, and his once enlarged glands had vanished. And his appetite knew no limits. "That's not the way to eat your dinner!" Sister was heard to cry. "Haven't you got a knife and fork?" Chips, ice-cream, strawberry jam, and 'Tizer' were his favourites, and on this diet he rapidly made up the weight he had lost. The day came when he was ready to go home. His pyjamas and slippers were put in a small suitcase, and, with trousers, pullover, coat, and school cap, he walked slowly through the hospital gates between his mother and father.

That was two years ago. Since then Jimmy has had another Christmas, and two birthdays, two Easters, and five school holidays. He was happy enough before his illness, but each month his parents tried to bring him even more happiness, knowing that it might be his last. Thrice more he walked out through the hospital gates. But the fourth time he was carried by his father, and last week he died.

Philosophers may argue that two years is a fleeting moment in the life of a little boy; that he might have found a greater peace in death two years ago than in two years hence; that a single sorrow borne once is lighter than many borne often. But the light in the eyes of Jimmy and his parents knew nothing of philosophy. We have no regrets.

Jane was a bright young lady of 3½ years who peered through the bars of the cot and never missed anything that went on in the ward. When she had been there for two or three months, and was by far the oldest inhabitant, the paediatrician suddenly struck his brow with his palm and declaimed: "Jane must have occupational therapy." The registrar and houseman set to work, and at last persuaded the unwilling occupational therapist to venture into the children's ward – an unprecedented feat.

Next day the houseman called on Jane, and found her with a little tin on her knees. The tin was neatly labelled "Occupational Therapy". "What's this, Jane?" he asked.

"Rubbish," she said.

# XIV

# Old People

IN these modern days when non-accidental injury has extended to wives, husbands, grannies, and even family pets, may I report a new variation, the battered doctor? I do not have in mind the traumas inflicted on public-spirited doctors who are roughly pushed aside by enthusiastic first-aiders rushing to get at an accident case. No, I mean it quite literally. For example, I have just met two young house-officers, one with cracked ribs and the other with a bruised thigh. Both had been assaulted in the casualty department. Yet another is a GP friend who is sporting a black eye received from a patient with painful piles – no longer on his list I need hardly add – who thought he had been kept waiting too long at the surgery.

I am not sure whether these are isolated incidents or a description of a new syndrome. Probably neither. In my own medical career I have been knocked out on three occasions. Once as a young doctor by a large Glasgow labourer in delirium tremens; once by a youngster, manic with meningitis; and lastly by a very old lady who weighed about seven stones. I was escorted to her house by a massive policeman following reports that she was in need of care and attention. She opened the door to my knock, looked me up and down, and before I could utter a word, laid me low with a formidable punch. As I collapsed into the arms of the officer, who was prudently standing behind me, I heard him say, as from a distance, "I forgot to tell you, doctor. She is a wee bit obstreperous."

IT was my first week as consultant cardiologist. The first patient I was asked to see on the urology ward was an 85-year-old man with a heart pacemaker. Could I advise about his fitness for a general anaesthetic? "Well, sir, I hear you've got a pacemaker," I started. "No doctor," said the man, "I've got two" – and clutched both pectorals, one in each hand. He had two, too. I didn't understand. Certainly there felt as if there were two generator boxes buried under the skin.

One of the surgeons wondered if one pacemaker was for the left ventricle, and the other for the right. Other explanations occurred to me: perhaps two were necessary for his balance – to stop him leaning to one side? Certainly in this hospital they didn't do anything by halves! I was impressed – they weren't leaving anything to chance. And I supposed, in these days of technological advance, that back-up systems might be necessary. But I did wonder what the hospital accountant would think.

As it turned out, the first pacemaker was implanted in 1974 and was a Lucas induction coil powered by external batteries. In 1978 the pacemaker failed, and a standard ventricular pacemaker was inserted in the opposite side, the induction coil being left in situ. These Yorkshiremen never part with anything!

IT can be embarrassing to turn up for a domiciliary visit and find that the patient has died and no-one has told you. Once I arrived in the middle of the post-interment festivities, which, in this part of the world, are conducted in a manner and on a scale which Homer would have appreciated. So grand are they that I could not but approve of one old lady who insisted that her obsequies were to be held ante-mortem, because she had not the least intention of being a totally passive participant in what, from her status in the local community, was bound to be a magnificent occasion.

The other day I received a request to visit a Mr B, aged 93. The details were vague, and I had little idea why I had been asked to visit. Knocking at the front door brought no results, so I went round to the back to find an elderly lady in the garden gazing up into the sky. I introduced myself, and said I had come to visit Mr B. "Ah!" said the lady, "he's up there", a finger pointing heavenwards.

I began to utter the usual platitudes one drags out on these occasions, but I was cut short by objects descending on me from above. A first tentative thought that they might be divine thunderbolts proved wrong: they were apples. Close inspection revealed Mr B ensconced some 15 feet up in a large apple tree, vigorously shaking the branches to shed the fruit which, to his disgust, he was now unable to reach and pick directly, due to some slight infirmities of age.

SHE was 78 and more than a little confused. It was difficult to picture her youthful, agile, riding a "rosin-back" and going through what she described as "hoops and all that". As she was leaving the clinic she suddenly turned. "Are you from Sanger's," she asked, "or Bertram Mills?" Sister was delighted; not every patient recognises me as a trick-cyclist.

OVER the phone, one December evening, the senior surgical registrar gave me details of the patient, who had an irreducible umbilical hernia with obstructive symptoms. "She's very deaf, but we got the history from her daughter who, by the way, is 84 years old." There was a slight pause and, almost apologetically, he added, "The patient herself is 102."

On my way to the hospital I was preoccupied with the calculation of homoeopathic doses of drugs, and eventually she received a tenth the amount of intravenous barbiturate that had been given to the previous young robust patient. As the needle entered the vein, strains of *Abide with Me* wafted along the corridor from a concert in a nearby ward, and it is to be hoped that my registrar did not notice the slight tremor in my hand.

All went well. In nine months' time the patient may well be enjoying her 103rd birthday as much as we did our post-op cup of coffee. For it was then that we remarked the details on her admission sheet. At the top of the page, after her name, was written: "Age – 102; Occupation – Factory Worker". We confidently expect that she will soon be fit to resume work.

"No, thank you," said Giles, when I offered him a salted peanut. This was strange as nuts are amongst his favourite titbits. Moreover, his sweet tooth is a source of wonder to his friends, conflicting as it does with so many of his nutritional theories. He explains it away by referring to a deprived childhood and although he can almost bring tears to the eye, his own as well as others, I know for a fact that his early years were quite sheltered and he had a doting aunt who refused him practically nothing. He counteracts the confectionery, he says, by using fluoride toothpaste.

His present aversion to nuts stems from a series of visits to the home of an elderly patient. As she left she would always present him with a small bag of brazil nuts, a source of particular delight. To give him his due, Giles always protested, as he knew she could ill afford such a luxury. At his last visit he persisted in this vein a little longer than usual. Slightly exasperated, the old lady said he must not worry. They were, in fact, a present from her son but, as she had no teeth, all she could do was suck the chocolate off the outside. "No" continued Giles sadly, "not even a peanut, thank you."

Not so long ago I was summoned to a local authority old people's home by a highly agitated matron. I was told, in a voice filled with horror, that Alec had proposed marriage to Ivy, and had been accepted. This seemed to be a perfectly reasonable, indeed laudable, state of affairs. I could think of no reason for matron's agitation – other than my private knowledge that she herself had carelessly omitted to involve either a minister of religion or a registrar before cleaving unto the man who shared her flat. So I inquired why the business of Alec and Ivy was so terrible.

It was explained to me, patiently, that Alec was very fit, had been married previously, and, what was more, was an ex-naval man. Thus he would, it was felt, wish to exercise his conjugal rights to the fullest extent. Ivy was a spinster, and could not, the staff felt sure, have any idea of what was coming to her.

It was my duty as a psychiatrist, I was told, to certify this man and, by incarcerating him in hospital, prevent him having his evil way with this innocent maiden. This, of course, I refused. However, I found myself manoeuvred into the position of having to find out whether Ivy knew the facts of life, and of enlightening her if she did not.

I chatted to her for a while about Alec, and then cautiously – after all, she was old enough to be my mother – asked her if she realised that there was something Alec would definitely want from her beyond mere companionship and platonic friendship. Her eyes sparkled with pleasure and excitement as she answered, "Oh, Yes!" I gave my blessing to the union and withdrew.

Alas, it was not to be. Officialdom would not tolerate the situation, especially when chivvied by Ivy's family, which saw its long-awaited, if modest inheritance slipping from its grasp. Alec was moved to another home and no contact, not even letters, was allowed between the two sweethearts.

A few weeks later, Ivy died, still a virgin.

Our community psychiatric nurses are an intrepid lot – they have to be, because they work with the elderly who can, at times, be pretty formidable. Often the difficulties are compounded because it is unclear which member of the household ought to be the patient.

Recently we received an urgent call from the elderly companion of Miss X, a new patient on our books. The companion had not seen Miss X that day, her bedroom door was locked on the inside, and shouting and hammering evoked no response. One of our sisters took Bill, a young enrolled nurse on our staff, and set off for the flats in which the couple lived. Sister decided to send Bill to peer in through the bedroom window; as the flat was a couple of floors up, he had to clamber along a narrow ledge from the adjacent sitting-room window. This he did. On looking in he was quite sure the room was empty, so back he went along the ledge to report to his superior. Sister was unimpressed. It was only too obvious, she explained patiently, that Miss X must be lying unconscious behind or under the bed. He must go back and effect an entry to the room. Sighing heavily, Bill traversed the ledge once more and, after managing to open the window, slid into the room. It was empty. Bill tried the door and found that, contrary to report, it was unlocked. He started to step into the little hall.

At this point the kitchen door opened and out came Miss X, fully dressed and anything but unconscious. Demands for an explanation for Bill's presence in her bedroom were lent a certain cogency by the regular, frequent, and forceful impingement of a large handbag on any portion of his anatomy that came within range – a handbag which, Bill maintains, was filled with concrete. There was no need of a neurological examination; he could confirm that Miss X possessed good muscle power and tone and has no signs whatsoever of intention tremor.

Later it transpired that Miss X, though a bit forgetful, was mentally far better than her companion, who was firmly fixed somewhere around 1922. The companion remained convinced, however, that Bill had effected a daring rescue of Miss X, and showed her appreciation at Christmas by giving him a calendar – two years out of date, it is true, and it was Easter, not Christmas, but the thought was there.

Mrs Bodgers fixed the student attached to the geriatric unit with a gimlet · eye that had lost nothing for being 91 years old. "Young lady," she snapped, "why are you asking me these ridiculous questions? Do you think I am stupid?" I saw the girl write, "Uncooperative, probably senile", across the mental test questionnaire that she had been trying in a pedantic way to administer, before withdrawing with all the outraged hauteur that today's young people manifest if they are crossed.

My sympathies were all with Mrs Bodgers. To have someone sit down by your bed and solemnly ask you the date, your birthday, the prime minister's name, the sovereign's name, and – the item that would spark rebellion in me for the very good reason that I would make an unholy mess of it – serial sevens, seems to me downright insulting. It's bad enough for those who know the answers, but for someone who is aware that her memory is failing to have it so publicly displayed is wanton cruelty. My scientifically minded colleagues will say, "It is necessary to have a standardised format to enable us to quantify the degree of memory impairment and measure any changes." Is it? What does it prove? If someone can demonstrate to me that, say, not knowing the PM's name means one cannot make a cup of tea, that a failure to do serial sevens correlates with an inability to do baked beans on toast, that patients who cannot remember the name of the sovereign forget to wash, then I might just be interested. But, so far, no-one has done this.

I tried to talk to the student later, pointing out that, by chatting quietly with Mrs Bodgers, I had managed to elicit answers to all the general knowledge questions and gain a wide overall idea of her mental ability without using the standard form. (I did not say that, in finding out the name of the prime minister, I accepted "That Woman!!" as a correct answer.) The girl was not impressed – after all, I am only a psychiatrist – and dismissed my approach as non-scientific. I decided not to go too deeply into the scientific basis of pencil-and-paper tests so I trotted out about making cups of tea as above, only to be told Mrs Bodgers was quite useless in the kitchen. How, I wondered, could the girl know? She had seen the report of the occupational therapy assessment. I gave up; how could I begin to explain to this self-assured child the difference between the ultramodern ceramic hob and built-in electric oven in the kitchen where the tests had been done and the old range on which Mrs Bodgers (and her mother before her) had cooked for a family? But I should have tried; in ten years that girl might be my GP.

We made an interesting foursome. On one side of the table sat the GP and his health visitor, both perched on the edges of their chairs, with all the hesitancy and distaste of elderly maiden ladies in a public convenience. On the other side sat the patient and I, much more comfortably – Mrs X because it was her house, and me because I have long ceased worrying about my clothes. Not that there was any real cause for anxiety; the house was scruffy, grubby even, but not actually dirty or insanitary. The GP and health visitor were determined that the patient should go into hospital. She was equally determined not to go, and I was on her side.

As usual on such occasions, food was brought into the argument. I was informed by the health visitor that Mrs X compiled a weekly shopping list and that it, together with her pension book, was sent down to the village store cum post office. The order, plus the balance of her pension, was delivered by the shopkeeper every Thursday evening. The arrangement seemed very satisfactory and I gazed, perplexed, at the order-book thrust under my nose, vainly trying to discover what reprehensible secrets it held. Bread, butter, cheese, cereals, tin of sardines, two slices of ham or tongue – it seemed a veritable feast compared with the diet of many patients. The health visitor was exasperated: "Look," she said, in the voice she reserved for talking to subnormal mothers about their babies, "she is ordering a tin of fruit and a tin of cream every week!" Mrs X pointed out that fruit and cream was her Sunday treat (admittedly her memory was failing, and sometimes she had her Sunday treat on a Saturday). I supported her, suggesting she had a perfect constitutional right to fruit and cream every day if she chose, a remark greeted with contemptuous snorts from opposite. Evidently, fruit and cream on Sunday turned the house into a one-woman den of iniquity as far as the two professionals were concerned.

The patient did not go into hospital. Our nurses visited regularly, and everything carried on – fruit, cream, and all – for three years. But the other morning, the GP rang me. "Your nurses need not bother," he said, "to call on Mrs X today. My health visitor noticed her curtains were still drawn, we broke in, and found her dead in bed. Must have died in her sleep." How nice for her, I commented, only to be shaken out of my seat by a blast down the phone. "You," snarled the GP, "are a disgrace to the profession. If you had taken her into hospital when we begged you, she would still be alive today. You should be ashamed of yourself!"

But I'm not.

THOUGH I am opposed to the principle of private homes for the elderly, there are some whose levels of care and tolerance are way above what might be expected. In my patch this is particularly true of St Bernadette's – a small conventual group of nuns, caring, with a devotion that has to be seen to be believed, for some of the most unlovable people imaginable. A cry for help from there means a real problem, and when asked recently to do a domiciliary visit, I wondered what was in store.

I was met by Sister Mercy – little, bubbling, always cheerful. Today she looked worried. Mr Bloggs was their problem. He had not moved from his bed for many years, and the good sisters had waited on him assiduously all this time; now he was becoming even more demanding and difficult, and they had agreed, reluctantly, to seek my opinion.

When I talked to him I could not bring myself to like him. He was a lazy, shiftless man, with a long history suggestive of severe personality disorder, and it seemed to me he was quite content to lie around and be attended to by the poor nuns. As I knew it was not in them to be firm with him, I decided that I would admit him for a couple of weeks to get my staff to give him a thorough working-over; I knew they would mobilise him.

I merely told Sister Mercy I would admit him that day. "Thanks be, doctor," she said, "you see, we are worried that the poor man has not opened his bowels for simply ages." I inquired further. He refused to leave his room, I was told, and bedpans were never used by him. I eyed the large Victorian mahogany press standing in one corner of the room and sniffed cautiously. "I think," said Sister Mercy, "all the dear man's things that he'll be needing to take to hospital are in here", and she advanced upon the press.

Being more worldly than her I left the room quickly. But as I shut the door a very uncharacteristic expletive from Sister Mercy (and one which, I would imagine, must have figured large when she next confessed) told me she had solved for herself the mystery of his apparent total constipation.

OLD Mrs D suddenly became confused and semiconscious for no reason that I could discover. There had been a previous gas leak and daughter was disturbed about the smell in the house. We both had catarrh and were unsure, and as meter was next door to an open fire I phoned the Gas Board and also arranged a domiciliary visit. Consultant, Gas Board, and I arrived simultaneously. Much sniffing of the air as consultant examined patient and could find no obvious cause for her condition – at the same time Gas Board fitted elaborate apparatus and reported no leak to be found. Coming, still sniffing, downstairs, association of smell suddenly struck both of us, and we rushed up again to confirm that the old lady's breath was loaded with acetone – daughter meanwhile saying, for first time, "she's been drinking buckets of water for last few weeks – is it diabetes?" The Gas Board was left to continue its investigations next door – none of us having the face to admit the true cause of the smell. Mrs D and her diabetes came under control very quickly and she is home again now.

# XV

# Hatches and Despatches

ANYTHING that reminds us of the human frailty that underlies all organisation is always refreshing; it prevents us from becoming too pompous. Having occasion to visit the Department of Health not long ago, and my mind not being wholly on the matter that had brought me there, I found myself musing on the changes in the past few years. It suddenly struck me that the monolithic pile that houses my hospital department is quite literally built on a piece of innocent credulity that will serve to keep it humble for years. Not so very long ago, as a student, I did my first domiciliary obstetrics case in a slum house exactly where the department now stands. She was a totter's wife having her fourth, and ably assisted in the business by her 17-year-old daughter, Julie. I clothed the inevitable embarrassment of waiting with little to do and less to say by staring out of the window, and I noticed that at the end of the grimy yard a fresh bunch of flowers had been laid underneath a plane tree. I was told that this very day was Julie's birthday, and the custom was to put flowers annually on the grave of her twin, who was born dead and laid there to rest. Julie had been born first, closely followed by the "twin", which the midwife had wrapped in newspaper and told them to bury at the bottom of the garden. Even I, crass student as I then was, had the wit to hold my peace and not to tamper with people's beliefs. So smile a little, you in your offices, and continue gentle.

EACH year I write to the survivors of our penicillin trials for bacterial endocarditis to see how they are getting along. One of the most faithful of my flock is a woman who has moved away from our district. In 1954 she wrote that she was doing well. She was sure I would be pleased to know that a few months ago she gave birth to a baby and that both she and the child were flourishing. Indeed she was so satisfied, she said, that she intended visiting a heart specialist to see if she was strong enough to get married.

WE have just opened our new family planning clinic. The motto suggested for it was "How to try without really succeeding".

ANSWERING a call for an anaesthetist recently, I was met by a young, breathless, and obviously perturbed nurse. "I'm afraid the patient has delivered precipitately, doctor!" was her opening remark. I said mildly that such things had been known to happen, and that there was no need to get upset. "But she delivered while she was sitting on the toilet!" was the rejoinder. I explained that this was a somewhat rarer, but by no means unknown, subgroup of precipitate deliveries. This diminished her agitation, but she asked for my help in completing the form recording the condition of the infant. Her gratitude seemed oddly tinged with doubt when she found later that my answer to the question about the infant's colour was "Pink, but not flushed."

THERE is a long track to the cottage. A dog yaps from a derelict car; chickens scratch the yard. In the one downstairs room there is a venerable stove, a churn of stream water, a guitar hung on a nail, and a small boy being read fairy stories by a neighbour. Upstairs, Mummy is in her 14th hour of labour and now, says the midwife, "fully dilated".

Mother's pains are infrequent. She's tetchy at the midwife's exhortations and with her man for rubbing the wrong spot on her back. Times passes. Nothing happens. Dusk creeps up, cold and beautiful. Mother walks, squats, tries all-fours. "Oh this wretched baby!" She complains. The midwife mentions hospital: twenty miles and a world away.

I've been given – or remembered – few words of obstetric wisdom. The wisest were: "Leave be." Birth is a natural process. So we persuade the mother on to her side, cradled by her man, to rest. I join the little boy for *Peter Rabbit*. Shortly comes a hearty cry of progress. "I can't deliver her like this," the midwife confides. "Why ever not? When I was a lad most mothers were delivered in the left lateral pos . . ." No time to explain: here's the crown and mother's panting concern that those downstairs make the finale in time. They do – thanks to the cord twice round that baby's neck. The most joyful of sounds, a first cry, banishes our nightmares. Fingers are counted, orifices peered into, the hasty thump of her new heart sounded, and then Naomi is returned to the breast.

Leave be. The chickens are at roost, the dog and the day asleep. I have a conceit that I'm for righting things that do not happen "naturally" and that the occasions when I'm not needed are but happy accidents. Nature knows better. It teaches doctors they must not seek to justify themselves by making crises where none, in Nature's perspective, exist. It is a hard lesson for us to learn: "Leave be."

BOTH were elderly, both were dying. I think both knew it. Mrs X was 83 and had cancer. She was afraid of dying – afraid of pain, distress, indignity. Tommy X was 16 – a good age for a labrador which, as far as he was capable of being defined, was what he most resembled. He lay on the foot of his mistress's bed, just raising a grizzled head when I entered. He sniffed my proffered hand, decided I meant no harm and settled down again, watching me out of the whites of his eyes. Everyone thought Mrs X should be in hospital. She had no close family. It was not right for her to be alone – she was at risk, it was explained to me. She refused to go anywhere, partly because of Tommy and partly because she wanted to die at home.

But I was under orders to compel her admission to hospital under the Mental Health Act. A Greek chorus of general practitioner, district nurse, home-help supervisor, and meals-on-wheels organiser sat in the next room, listening to our conversation and interjecting remarks like, "We can arrange to dispose of the dog" and "She must go somewhere and be looked after properly – anything could happen if she stays here." The meals-on-wheels lady played her trump card: "She's not eating properly. She gives most of the meals we bring to that damned dog." I murmured that, from what I had seen of the meals-on-wheels in our area, that was a matter for the RSPCA, not me. Some 3 minutes later, having worked out what I meant, the chorus was reduced by one as the meals organiser left, slamming the door behind her. I refused, of course, to use compulsory admission and offered to help support her at home. I departed with angry words from GP and district nurse.

What happened eventually? The GP ordered an ambulance, bullied Mrs X into it, and sent her off to casualty. She lay there for a time, before being found a bed on a medical ward. A full investigative programme was planned, to tell everyone what they knew already, but Mrs X signified her refusal to cooperate by dying in the night. And Tommy? They went to collect him next morning, with an appointment booked at the nearest vet. But the body huddled at the bottom of the empty bed was cold.

WE were overwhelmed by the response to our advertisement for a mortuary attendant. They telephoned, they wrote, they persuaded the porter at the lodge of their bona fides, and appeared in person in the hall. Many had not the remotest idea what the job involved. One had spent the last eight years as a sheet-metal worker. Another offered us fluent Arabic, Italian, French, and Hindustani, forgetting that in a mortuary these would all fall on deaf ears. The man who had served much of his life in a borough cleansing department had perhaps an inkling. And so had the man who wrote in to ask what sort of work the job "entrailed". But what were the chances of the candidate whose only qualification apparently was that he was "jolly"? "Sir," wrote another, "I have been for six years a courier in the Foreign Office." That Mercury should ever become elderly and apply for the job of ferryman on the Styx!

Of those who turned up in the flesh, and departed in it creeping, we specially liked the ex-prize-fighter. "And what experience," we asked warily, our eyes traversing his monstrous hulk, "have you had of handling bodies?" "Well," he said modestly, flexing his muscles and swaying slightly on his heels, "I've laid out a few . . ." Wistfully we rejected a vision of his arriving in a ward and saluting Sister with hands clasped triumphantly above his head. We said we'd let him know.

The feverish secretary darted out to intercept yet another stranger in the hall. Sombrely suited this one, and filling his shoulder-pads much less aggressively. He had nice ears. She warmed to him. No, he replied coldly to her friendly query. He had not come about the job. He was a consultant surgeon from another hospital and would she kindly conduct him to Dr White?

IT is not often that a demand from the Inland Revenue brings a smile to the lips, but that is what happened recently at our university. A missive arrived addressed to "William Hunter, Surgeon". In it the tax inspector stated he had been unable to trace a tax return for the said William Hunter. A reply was requested within 14 days on pain of dire consequences.

Our campus wag replied. The surgeon in question was no longer in active practice, he said. At least, not as far as could be ascertained. As to his whereabouts: some said he was in one place, others somewhere else. One member of staff, a physician, was convinced that Hunter was enduring the rigours of a particularly hot climate and should not be further distressed by such communications. Another, from the divinity faculty, said he would try to contact him but could hold out little hope of success. However, our correspondent concluded they had forwarded the letter to an old university colleague, Adam Smith, who had a building nearby.

NOWHERE have I seen a mention of the benefit of having a friend who insists on looking on the gloomy side of things. It is not that we are heartless towards human suffering. News of deaths, disasters, crises, and illnesses can be a real tonic. When my mother was feeling depressed after a fall followed by weeks of pain and stiffness, she wrote to an aunt who replied saying she would like to come for a few days. Knowing my aunt's propensity for deaths, funerals, and nursing people in their last days, and her detailed accounts of the illnesses of all her friends, I thought to myself that she was the very last visitor I would recommend just then. But not a bit of it! The evening she arrived I lingered awhile and heard details of the elderly neighbour's most recent attack of bronchitis up to the reading of the will. Then came an argument on the exact hour of my great-grandmother's death. Apparently, what set the time finally in my aunt's mind was the recollection that her grandson had taken the old lady's lunch up on a tray, and found that she had passed away. This visit did my mother a world of good. Everyone felt greatly cheered by her visit. It is not always the exhortation to "pull yourself together" that is most effective in times of depression.

IN the course of my work for the coroner I travel over a good many miles of country, and the other day I was sent to an early Victorian workhouse, standing in open fields. The mortuary's post-mortem room has a french window opening on to a garden, and is provided with a small oak prie-dieu. On this I noticed a venerable looking volume bound in ancient calf. It was John Wesley's *Hymns for the use of the people called Methodists*, dated 1797. Wesley states that in these hymns there is no doggerel, no feeble expletives, nothing turgid or bombast, no cant expressions or words without meaning, and that they show in the purity, strength and elegance of the English language the true spirit of poetry which must be the gift of Nature. Turning over the pages I found a funeral hymn, the first verse of which expressed sentiments I thought particularly appropriate to the coroner's pathologist:

> "Ah! Lovely appearance of Death
> What sight upon Earth is so fair,
> Not all the Gay Pageants that breathe
> Can with a dead body compare.
> With Solemn delight I survey
> The Corpse, when the Spirit is fled,
> In love with the beautiful clay
> And longing to lie in its stead."

AN inoffensive little man walked into our hospital not long ago to inquire about the procedure for bequeathing his body for medical research. A helpful porter directed him to the mortuary.

Monday is one of my "do-good" days, a phrase no one likes, conjuring up as it does a picture of somewhat obese, well-meaning, middle-aged, middle-class ladies in twin sets and pearls. And how misleading. In my particular sphere we are a motley bunch of all ages, sizes, and shapes and just about all possible backgrounds. George drives vast tankers and Sarah has been supported (?) by the State since she escaped from her battering husband. She's certainly got no pearls, and nobody, including himself, would describe George as middle-class.

One advantage of manning a help line is that clients come to *you* when feeling in need of an ear or a hand. You don't approach them. The other is having unlimited time. It's nice, of course, if callers later let you know how they've got on, and occasionally they do, like the youngster who had gone through a very bad patch a while ago and rang last week to tell me how fantastic things were now.

"And what about your parents?" I asked. "How are things with them?"

"Just fab," she said, "mind you, my dad's pretty strict. He said he'd kill me if I ever took another overdose." The threat of suicide is a serious business.

# XVI

# Cussed Machinery

ARRANGEMENTS had been carefully made: the patient's notes had been reviewed; her husband informed by telephone of the time of the expected visit; and the ECG machine borrowed. Thus, it was with some confidence and interested anticipation that the new consultant set out on his first domiciliary visit. With shrewd foresight, he had bought a map of the town. The first small setback came when the patient's road failed to appear on the map or, indeed, in the index. After a 20-minute drive around roads of similar, but not identical, name, the consultant was forced to telephone the patient's husband. Directions were provided and, within minutes, the lost cardiologist was trundling through the patient's front door armed with all necessary apparatus.

A tortuous walk through a hall of many colours was rewarded with a sight of the patient, a stout and talkative lady in her late 60s. The visitor's remaining confidence was rapidly dispersed by the patient's inability either to listen to or to answer any of his questions. The chief medical problem could equally have concerned her mastectomy, vitiligo, thyroid disease, removal of fibroid, angina, drop attacks, blackouts, or general nervousness. One comforting feature was that the patient's constitution was clearly strong enough to cope with all these complaints.

The ECG machine was placed, with an appropriate flourish, on the bed. But its lid remained firmly closed, despite vigorous attempts to prise it open. Fortunately, an idle movement of the case while searching for a handkerchief to wipe the brow resulted in an opening of the lid and offered the possibility of continuing the investigation.

Application of the electrodes and jelly was unusually straightforward, and indeed would have been entirely successful had not the recording apparatus failed to produce more than a few idle twitches, despite twiddling all of its many knobs. With keen diagnostic skill the cardiologist perceived the condition of exhausted batteries (a condition he shared), so he was forced to leave the apparatus assembled and return to the car for a mains connector. Conspiracy between the physician and the patient's husband eventually produced sufficient leads, plugs, and adaptors to impart 50 cycles to the ECG machine and a degree of responsiveness in the electronics hitherto unseen.

The patient's main complaint (finally identified to be her recent drop attacks) was attributed to vertebrobasilar insufficiency. It was rewarding to learn that her GP had established this diagnosis several months earlier.

DURING the refresher course a young consultant physician demonstrated the latest electrical teaching equipment and monitoring devices to reproduce all abnormal heart sounds and patterns. An oscilloscope showed an ECG tracing, carotid-pulse wave-pattern, and two recordings of the heart-sounds on a radar-like screen; a phonocardiosimulator reproduced variations in the amplitude, duration, volume of the heart-sounds and murmurs. Both were working at full pressure, and together they filled the hall with sound and vision. The patient was in a nearby room, but within hearing-distance. A GP asked "Can you suppress the breath sounds?" The consultant replied, "Yes, quite easily", and turning towards the patient's room, he cupped his hands to form a megaphone and yelled, "Mr Smith, please hold your breath for one minute."

A COMPLICATION of DC defibrillation which is, I believe, as yet unpublished was brought to light not long ago in our hospital. Our defibrillator, mounted on a red-painted trolley, is widely known as the "fire-engine". When a patient collapsed on the ward a nurse shouted to the ward clerk to send for the fire-engine. This message was relayed to the hospital switchboard operator, who had not previously met the expression. Three minutes later four fire appliances attempted to enter the hospital courtyard. Simultaneously a fire-float, hoses at the ready, cruised into the basin of the docks alongside the hospital. Fortunately, the fire brigade felt that the exercise had been a useful practice, and the patient had not, in fact, suffered a cardiac arrest.

I MET a urologist the other day in a fine state of elation. In the face of extreme technical difficulty he had succeeded in re-establishing drainage from the solitary kidney of a very ill patient: not only was the blood-urea now coming tumbling down, it looked like reaching normal precisely on the day when a visiting Urological Society would provide the ideal captive audience. Two days later, the picture was one of gloom. A ward maid on her evening hoovering round had dislodged the ureteric catheter, which then disimpacted itself from the collecting apparatus and fell on to the floor, to come to rest finally in a sequestered position in the dust-bag. A nil return for output brought the situation to light next day, but by this time the blood-urea was rising again, and the sweet taste of technical triumph was soured.

I found the junior staff shaking their heads sadly over such defeatism. Any registrar worth his urinary chloride, they thought, would have immediately roughed out for *The Lancet* a paper entitled "Failure of Electric Suction Apparatus to Facilitate Drainage from the Renal Pelvis".

I WOULD like to offer some thoughts on the Common Micturition Policy or CMP. The policy has had to be introduced because demand for urine by the woollen industry has dropped alarmingly. What a change from a century or two ago. Then it was common practice for urine to be used to extract the grease from wool. In very hot weather and times of drought, some people diluted the pure substance! In the late 18th century, George McIntosh devised a hydrometer to enable collectors to assess the quality of the product accurately. Some collectors ensured a plentiful supply by seeing to it that patients drank plenty before surgeons cut for the stone – giving rise to the colloquial expression "getting stoned". Others took more drastic measures to obtain supplies. Two famous twins Cath and Ita, joined forces to take the urine out of people and invented the instrument named after them – the catheter. However, the final decision on a Standard Relief Charge will obviously be a political one with a capital P. It should be noted that the CMP has allowed the UK to retain pints and quarts as units of measurement. At the turn of the century there was a sharp reduction in the number of collection points, and collectors had to queue at peak flow times. This led to the police having to mind these Qs of Ps. More recently, our local council attached a notice stating "Wet Paint" to the P-for-parking sign. It is amazing how many of our local dogs can read and have carried out the instruction to the letter. The paint used had to be acid resistant, because $K_9P$ is even stronger than nitric acid. The best books for further details on the history of this aspect of plumbing are *Temples of Convenience* by Lucinda Lambton, *The Specialist* by Charles Sale, and *Clochemerle*, by Gabriel Chevalier.

Among my many faults an inability to spell must rank high. This did not matter, at one time, because I wrote everything by hand and a vague squiggle could conceal my uncertainties. This all changed a year or so back, when I was lured into buying a word processor. It has been very useful and I would not be without it – but the neatly printed text does show me up. Recently, therefore, I have invested in a spelling-checking program which not only checks my spelling but also suggests alternatives for words it does not recognise. Being innocent of much medical jargon, the machine has uttered some entertaining suggestions.

My first effort was a letter to Mr X, our unit general manager, to complain about the latest effects of the Griffiths report on the NHS. Mr X (UGM) became Mr X (Ugly), whilst Griffiths changed to Gruffness and NHS into NAG.

Then I tried writing to one of our surgeons about someone who had attended his outpatients ("outdated" the machine would have it). The man had had a barium enema, and anyone who has experienced one will appreciate the change to "baring enemy". I went on to discuss his inguinal hernia, vaguely wondering what the surgeon would make of "infernal hermit".

By now I was really getting into the swing of it, so I wrote to our local professor of obstetrics and gynaecology, who came out as professor of obituaries and gymnasium. That a paediatrician should become "patriarchal" seemed apt; the translation of our endocrinologist into "endearing" I was not so sure about. I felt sorry for our orthopaedic surgeon who, at the touch of a computer key, became an "orphaned" surgeon.

I suppose it is a comment on our times that much psychiatric terminology was in the program's dictionary: schizophrenia, paranoid psychosis, addiction, it recognised the lot. But it made a very appropriate job of addressing our highly qualified senior psychiatrist: Dr Z, MD, FRCPsych, became Dr Z, Mad, Frantic.

I have drawn a number of champagne corks in my time, and I have been among oenophiles often enough to take pride in the *méthode prudente* (cork away silently and a couple of glasses poured out before the $CO_2$ notices that it is free) rather than the *méthode flamboyante* (pop whoosh! But, darling, a slipperful is what you *should* have!). It was sinful pride for me to say with a modest hint of competence, "Oh, I think I can control the *cork*", when I was advised where the windows were, and if the devil was asleep no doubt one of his minions shook the bottle briskly before handing it to my confident skill. Until the plasterer comes again, the ceiling has a lovely memorial chipped out of it to mark my arrogance.

DOCTORS have long shown an interest in injuries from champagne corks. I refer to their treatment, not their causation. In our hospital, in opulent days long gone by when beer was provided gratis, crown-cork openers were always ignored once new members acquired the local technique. The bottle was grasped firmly, with the neck snugly encircled by all four fingers of the left hand; using the proximal interphalangeal joint of the left index finger as a fulcrum and the handle of a stout fork as a lever, the bottle could be opened with a pop to rival that of real champagne.

There were hazards, of course, failure being the most humiliating. The fork might bend, the lid might shift just enough to allow some beer to escape but not enough to pour it out, the whole neck of the bottle might break off, and the fulcrum finger, until it became adapted to its function, could become quite painful. With practice, the cap could be projected several feet to land in the soup of a favourite colleague. However, there was always the chance that the aim would be faulty. It was thanks to fortune, rather than skill, that there were no accidents to eyes among the occasional minor facial injuries.

ONE of my patients, a very young man of 80, was recounting to me his early motoring exploits.

He worked for a shoe salesman, and part of his duties was to deliver repaired shoes to the wilder parts of the Cumbrian fells and valleys. One Friday evening, the main business of the day being finished, his employer took him over Shap Fell and in one lesson taught him to drive. The next day he was sent out on his round by himself. On this first trip out he came across a steep hill, and the car failed to make it. Three times he had to reverse the car down "and I'd never reversed a car before". He then noticed a man standing in a field watching his misfortunes who gave him the following advice: "What tha wants to do is to turn its arse to t'ill." It worked.

Inquiry in the village revealed that the stranger who offered such sound advice was no other than the village idiot.

ALL was quiet in our coronary unit last Sunday morning, when the monitor suddenly showed that one of the temporary pacemakers was accelerating – 70 . . . 80 . . . 100 . . . 120/min. Sister rushed to the cubicle, where she found the patient half out of bed and struggling with the rate-control switch of her pacemaker. They looked at each other for a moment, but the patient took the initiative as she demanded, "How do you get music out of this damn thing?"

AFTER dinner someone told us of a spoof television programme, broadcast early one April, about the spaghetti-picking festival in Southern Italy, when the spaghetti is plucked from the trees and there are accompanying ceremonies and celebrations – all described in detail. Many people fell for this absurd tale; we all thought that an excellent joke. When we had done laughing at those gullible folk, our host asked, "But seriously, have you ever thought how they get the hole down the middle of the spaghetti?"

At this we all fell to suggesting means of making the holes, and much learning and ingenuity were exhibited. The mechanically minded among us proposed machines and processes that might succeed, and others spoke of the malleability, ductility, cohesiveness, and surface tension that would be needed in the pasta, and of the application of Poiseuille's formula to air passing along the hole as it expanded when the spaghetti was cooked. I (who have little physics but am something of a wag) suggested that they might make the hole first and then spray the pasta on to it.

In the cooler atmosphere of the next morning I began to wonder whether spaghetti actually does have a hole down the middle. Next time I have some I shall look; and if it doesn't I shall be very cross with our host for deceiving us with such a silly pointless question.

"It is not often I see you in bed with a cold," I said to Giles, when he stopped sneezing. "Have you given up taking vitamin C?" "Certainly not," he muttered thickly. "It's that dashed car that's to blame." "What?" I cried. I was taken aback, for Giles is intensely proud of his new automobile. It has all the latest gadgets: power steering, power brakes, automatic gears, a sun roof, anti-dazzle windscreen, additional headlights, electronic devices, stereo music from hidden cassettes, seats designed by an orthopaedic consultant which warm the bottom in winter, a compass which guides you to safety when lost; a metallic voice which tells everyone to fasten their seatbelts, and a discreet exterior of yellow and maroon.

Giles was delighting in his new acquisition when he espied some blemishes on its pristine surface. The birds had taken their customary revenge on the human race. Giles immediately swung into an adjacent car-wash. Pushing a button, he lowered the windows and, leaning out, put the requisite coins into the machine and then drove forward to the white line. The contraption started to come alive. He calmly watched the enormous green, soapy sodden rollers slowly approach his limousine, dripping water from every pore. They began to revolve. Giles languidly pressed the button to raise the windows. Unfortunately, nothing happened.

WE have an elderly friend who has been quite independent despite elevations of nearly all the bad things and depressions of most of the good ones. A few months ago she noted dizziness and a lightheaded feeling after driving for long periods.

"I'm not sure what it is," remarked her GP, "but it might be an incipient stroke." He ordered a lot of expensive tests including a brain scan. They were all normal. "You'll have to ask for some help with the driving" was his final recommendation.

But our friend, being an independent sort, wasn't quite ready for this, so she sought a second opinion – from her neighbour's son, aged 12. He listened to the story and then asked, "Can I see the car?"

A few minutes later he crawled out from underneath with a wad of foreign material that he had extracted from the exhaust pipe.

Our friend drives without difficulty now that the carbon monoxide problem has been solved. A pity the neighbour's son wants to be a car mechanic – he has the makings of a splendid diagnostician.

WE have been converted – not by any Divine afflatus but North Sea gas. After a couple of visits of inspection, the gang arrived and refitted us most efficiently. Alas, no gas flowed. The foreman asked me where the gas came into the house. "Search me," I replied. So the gang dug up the drive, the garden, and even the paddock. There was no success, so they summoned more assistance, including the boss. I suggested to him that it might have been prudent to find the inlet before converting the appliances. He deprecated this: "Let me assure you, Sir, that my men are leaving no stone unturned." I could only agree. Regretfully I re-entered our cold house and found the men all seated at the kitchen table, playing cards. My wife, always a diplomat, said it was a pity there was no gas or she would have made them a cup of tea. The foreman turned to the apprentice and told him to pop down to the works and fetch a "Calor" gas burner. Thus we survived the next few days until the inlet pipe was found. We had gas and all was well, which was lucky as there was a cold snap. Next evening I returned from my round to find the house icy. "I am sorry, dear," said my wife, "the gas board have just rung up to say that the valve at the sub-station has frozen and there will be no gas till it thaws."

# XVII

# Better Halves

SCIENTIFIC references which turn out to be "personal communications" are a tiresome form of conceit much loved by some authors. But I could not help being amused recently by a reference given by a British surgeon in an American journal. The reference was to a personal communication from the author himself and his wife. It was nice to know that they were speaking to each other, even if the event occurred two years before the article was published.

THE opening ceremony had been a great success. The Royal Personage was gracious; the weather was fine; my speech had been well received; the dinner had been brilliant. As we went to bed that night, my wife said, "I was very proud of you today." When I got up next morning, I said to her, "Are you still proud of me?" "No," she replied. "I'm all right now."

THE jets fly over our house with booming regularity, night and day. My wife was therefore very pleased when a drug company representative called and handed her a book about a Symposium on Reversible Airways Obstruction. Something was being done about it at last.

WOULD you give your wife a cookery book for her birthday? The question is not as simple as it may seem. It might be easier to stick to another half-dozen box of size-something nylons. Or a tiny phial of that exotic perfume, so seductively advertised with the allure of romance. Or the good old monster box of chocolates with the satin bow on top – which brings us back with a jerk to this question of your own tum as well as hers.

Just how objective can you be about this business of cookery books? The very idea is liable to raise nasty suspicions in her mind about your fidelity. Getting tired of what she has to offer, developing new appetites, hankering to taste more spicy cooking. I doubt whether you could talk yourself out of that one. But just suppose that you have been gifted with enough blarney to get away with it, and the new cookery book gets as far as the kitchen cabinet. Where is it going to get you? If you are a gourmet, you are doomed to disappointment. Her bouillabaisse will never have that genuine Provençal flavour, however much saffron she slaps on the fish. Her ravioli will not be as good as the stuff from a tin. Her smørrebrød would turn the stomach of the strongest Dane: her paella any Spaniard's. It will lead only to a lot of recrimination and a king-size box of antacid tablets on the bedside table. But if you are the other sort, and need your calories to make life bearable and keep up your strength, you will be saying goodbye to roast beef and Yorkshire pudding, porridge, and muffins. You will creep in through the front door sniffing apprehensively, as though hunting a gas leak, and fearing the worst. Identification at the table tends to bring on instant anorexia. Do not worry, escape will soon come. You will starve to death.

Take my advice and stick to the nylons. She can always change them for the right size.

COOKING is a gregarious business. With the other arts pleasure is not necessarily impaired – it may even be enhanced – by the lack of an audience. Not so with cooking. This reflection has been forced on me by my wife's absence from home for a week. On most domestic business I'm the ultimate fool: with the car I can hardly find the hole to fill with water; and when a nail has to be fixed in the wall, my thumb and the wall itself are likely to feel the hammer before the nail does. But with cooking it's different, and, given half a chance, I take control in the kitchen: this is my ground. So when my wife went away, I was confident of not starving. Now, a bare week later, I'm not so confident. My first meal on my own was a nicely balanced three-course affair: my last before her return has been beans devoured out of a tin. How commonly, I wonder, do those who live alone hover on the brink of malnutrition because they have no companion to keep alive their pride in cooking?

WHEN I started getting night sweats I felt I should at least attempt to sort it out for myself. I had always considered myself something of a diagnostician. I suppose most clinicians do. We remember those diagnostic triumphs of ours that defeated older, respected, and more experienced colleagues, but forget the failures.

I felt perfectly well and certainly did not have a cough. My weight was obstinately static and although doing a physical examination on oneself has its limitations I was unable to detect any obvious signs. I forget what fatuous excuse I made to my partner when I asked her to draw off some blood to send to the laboratory for a sedimentation rate. All results were normal. So was my chest X-ray.

When I tried to discuss it with my wife she did not take much interest. She did not seem to take much interest in anything. Fortunately, she had enough sense to go to her own doctor, who wisely and promptly investigated her thyroid. It was clearly abnormal. Starting her on thyroxine has cured my night sweats. Now it is I who reaches for the extra blanket at night.

WE have just moved home. And a more traumatic experience I cannot imagine. I have had to dispose of most of my treasured possessions. My keepsakes, memorabilia, inherited bric-à-brac, bargains, and paperbacks. My wife is ruthless. Once arrived, there is the problem of finding the simple necessities I take for granted. Things which once I reached for automatically are no longer there. They are lost. Some are in strange cupboards, others in suitcases, but most reside in large cardboard boxes. These dominate our lives and only now, weeks later, are they being completely unpacked.

Old habits die hard. I still find myself automatically driving along the routes to my old home and once, without thinking, I rolled up the path to the front door, admiring my roses. I was reminded of Norbert Weiner, creator of cybernetics, whose absentmindedness was legendary. When he changed house, he returned to his former home that same evening despite the carefully repeated instructions of his wife. The place was deserted and only then did Weiner remember they had moved. But to where? He noticed a small child hovering about. "Tell me, little girl," said the great man. "Do you happen to know where the Weiners now live?" "Yes, Daddy," came the reply. "Mummy knew you would forget and she sent me over to fetch you."

I HAVE just bought my pocket diary for next year and this time I am going to take special care in making forward entries and particularly in my use of abbreviations, for I have scarcely recovered from a terrible and expensive experience two years ago. I had thought to gain favour by remembering my wedding anniversary (which is in November) and when I bought my new diary I immediately made the entry "Wedding Ann" at the appropriate date, forgetting even to add the full stop which might have saved me. When after many months the anniversary arrived, I asked my wife which Ann it was whose wedding we were to attend. My wife has red hair. I shall find 50 megaton explosions mere chickenfeed.

THIS keep fit fad has gone far enough. My wife, who declares that I am too old for squash, too stiff for jogging, and too indolent for golf, has taken to walking me in the evening. I think she misses our old collie who died recently. Neither hail, rain, snow, nor cries for mercy deter her from this nightly ritual.

Her latest idea is to give me equipment which can be used in the office. This consists of a pair of impossibly taut springs with hand grips, a set of skipping ropes, and a yo-yo – the latter to help me relax. And with them comes a booklet, illustrated by an Adonis whose rugged features, bulging muscles, and fluorescent teeth inflict themselves upon me from the television screen from time to time. I cannot say I have used them much, preferring to tell my wife lies rather than endure the comments of my colleagues. However, one of my fellow labourers, a surgeon, sought to try them out. All went well until he tried the skipping ropes. At the 30th hop he ruptured his Achilles tendon. I think a leisurely stroll in the hospital grounds will suffice from now on.

WHILE we dealt with the patients in the morning surgery, our secretary was answering 30 or more calls on two incoming lines, jotting down the names and addresses of the next influenza victim. Then while we gulped down our coffee, she presided like a judge, dishing out sentences to the assembled partners. "Finally," said she, turning to David, already with a heavy list, "there's your wife." "Heavens," he said, "she surely does not want a *visit*?" "No," said our secretary, as ever calm and efficient, "a prescription will probably do for her."

AND how about the following from the *Transactions* of the Medical Society of London (1970): "This year the Society decided to admit ladies to the Fellowship . . . We look forward to their participation in the affairs of the Society . . ."

# XVIII

# Public Health

IF you own a snug wee cottage in a Scottish glen, you'll always have people dropping by and staying as long as they can. Now such folk will put up with a great deal of discomfort – and our bracing Scottish air and the local malt whiskies combine to produce instant anaesthesia the moment each visiting head touches our lumpy pillows. The only thing which shatters the visitor is the water-supply. It comes from a burn high up the mountain side. Although the water is cold and crystal clear under normal conditions, the moment – and we have many – it rains the water turns brown; and the greater the rain the deeper the colour. Now none of the locals give a hoot about drinking chocolate-coloured water, but the visitors' fears are hard to quell. But the good weather this past summer has muted the usual shrieks of horror. I have a theory, however, that the water in our glen is bad when clear and good for you when positively opaque. At any rate, before the rains finally came the glen's oldest inhabitant died unexpectedly and so did the local butcher. Coincidence? Maybe, but after years of performing carefully controlled experiments I delight in making such rash correlations. Perhaps it's the joy of realising the virtual impossibility of scientifically testing such hypotheses, or else I'm entering my dotage – or possibly it's just that water of ours.

As chairman of a branch of ASH, the anti-smoking campaign, I am used to occasional odd telephone calls. But the most bizarre was from a gentleman who apologised for ringing me up and hoped (pause) I would bear with him if his request for help was interrupted by short rests (pause) while he recovered his breath. He had had one lung removed and the other was not very healthy. His problem was that he worked in a small house where the boss and her deputy were both heavy smokers. As a result (pause) he was always having to be off sick, his protests were of no avail, and could I help? Who was his boss? I asked. The local health education officer, he replied.

"Sugar", said my Brazilian friend as he ladled four spoonfuls into his coffee, "is what makes coffee bitter if you don't put it into it."

WITH the increased emphasis these days on what is called "safer sex", I suppose it was inevitable that there would be a proliferation of slot-machines dispensing articles that, in the more modest days of my youth, were termed "rubber goods". I dare say it is very right and proper to encourage such protection, but I feel it ought to be made clear that these items do have a failure rate, especially if used with more enthusiasm than caution. However, one firm seems to have accepted responsibility for this, for I have just seen a slot-machine bearing a large label which reads: "Emergency Service: In the event of breakage, 'phone . . ."

COOKING by numbers threatens Derbyshire. Remember Bakewell tart, real Bakewell tart? I had always supposed that a good version could be had from short-crust pastry, raspberry jam, sugar, butter, eggs, and, of course, almonds ground and in essence. Such a recipe would certainly have done for Isabella Mary Beeton and her successors. J. Sainsbury plc is not in the Beeton class. What would Mrs B have made of: "wheat flour, sugar, apple and blackcurrant jam (contains gelling agent E440a; acidity regulators E330, E331; colours E122, E142; preservative E202), animal and veg-etable fats, blackcurrants, egg albumen, ground rice, apple pulp, skimmed milk powder, modified starch, soya flour, salt, preservative E202, glucose syrup, flavourings, colours E102, 110, citric acid, adipic acid"? And what, indeed, are we to make of it? Happily, codes are available, giving us pectin, citric acid and sodium citrates, carmoisine, green S, potassium sorbate, tartrazine, and sunset yellow FCF. Even more happily you can still get the real thing in the town itself.

HEALTH education starts early in the North-West resorts. The children's model village covered a wide range of activities – the church organ playing Widor for a wedding, a country club, and a biscuit factory. And, of course, a corner tobacconist. Proprietor, Wun Lung Soon.

A "gay lady" in one of the remoter villages had resisted the energetic persuasions of the venereologist, the social worker, and the magistrate, and refused treatment. The venereologist, anxious lest his clinic should rival in size a GP's surgery, inquired if I, as county medical officer, could deal with the lady as a "statutory nuisance" under the Public Health Acts. Whatever my private thoughts on how far the definitions of "dusts" or "water courses" might be stretched, I resisted the suggestion. As the lawyers in the county clerk's office are far too innocent to be consulted on matters of such delicacy, I turned to my chief public-health inspector, a man of wisdom and wit. Together we talked over whether the lady could be dealt with as plying an "offensive trade"; but no, she could hardly be regarded as a "tripe dresser" or a "bone-boiler". Nor indeed could we act on the legislation which covers workplaces which are not kept sufficiently ventilated: the lady worked anywhere under God's good sky. Eventually my colleague had an inspiration. "Could she not, Sir,' he asked, "under section 74 of the Public Health Act, 1961, be put down as a pigeon or other bird in a built-up area?"

# XIX

# Ward, Clinic, Theatre

Giles was definitely in shock when I met him outside the hospital. Do you remember, he said, how it was when a consultant was called into the ward for an opinion? Did I remember! The patient had to be prepared, the bed and locker made tidy, and the instrument tray, covered with a chaste white cloth, placed close to hand. Sister, of course, had to be placated. As the junior doctor I had to memorise the leading features of the complaint, have the case notes ready and up to date. The visitor had to be attended upon, from escorting him to the bedside to holding the towel when he washed his hands. The last feature of the ceremony was to walk with him to the door of the ward while he dropped pearls of wisdom before me. It was quite a performance.

Giles's chagrin was occasioned by a visit to a distant ward. He had been asked to give an opinion on an patient with rectal spasm. He entered the ward at the appointed time but no-one was there to greet him. Eventually he traced the duty doctor to a small room where he reposed in a bright red open-necked shirt, jeans, and sandals, all covered in a loose-fitting white coat. He finally remembered why Giles had been summoned and, after finishing his coffee, took Giles into the ward. He looked around the patients clustered beside the television set and, in a loud voice called out, "Hands up the guy with the sore backside!" The future is not what it used to be, said Giles, as I took him to the cafeteria for a resuscitative cup of tea.

A MARRIED couple, both in their nineties, were recently injured in a traffic accident in North Wales; he sustained a broken arm and she a fractured rib, and both had the inevitable "shock" and anxiety about one another's health. They were admitted to Wrexham War Memorial Hospital, where those in charge had the inspired kindness to admit them to neighbouring beds, in the corner of a male ward. I hope other hospitals will bend the rules in similar acts of concern for their patients.

SOME junior hospital jobs may have turned sour, but there are plenty more that can, and still do, make you feel a king. And what about the "fun in sending death back where he came from"? Surely there's more fun there now than there ever was 50 years ago, and it must feel just as good now as it did then. Even the slight lump in the throat must be the same. No, there's no bitter taste here.

But think of some of my friends who left school on the same day as me. Some of them now have quite good jobs in industry. They have a nice office of their own, with a door that fits and does shut out the sound, with a carpet, with a desk (with drawers), and a telephone of their own, and usually a secretary. So what? They chose industry, and we chose medicine, for better for worse. Never mind the richer or poorer; and don't think I'm obsessed with material considerations. But think how much better it might be if we had some of the basic paraphernalia which they would consider essentials. If we have to write a letter, we sit down and write it out longhand. We may even sit at the same table or desk that you sat at 50 years ago. As likely as not we are sitting either in a small office shared with Sister (and often as small as 5 × 10 feet); or else we are sitting in the middle of the open ward.

What business concern which conducted its affairs like this would survive today? And if it's not good enough for them, why is it good enough for us? Think what we could do if we had their facilities. We have been trained to practise medicine, not to be secretaries or clerks. No, the house-job hasn't turned sour, and the taste is still good. The trouble is that we don't often get a taste of the real thing, except diluted.

I SHOULD like to assure my young peripatetic colleague (see above) who shares an office with Sisters "often as small as 5 × 10 feet" that in my day also Sister loomed much larger than life, but his example beats all our yesteryear dragons.

A 33-year-old woman was admitted to hospital for treatment of psoriasis. She was also known to suffer from afternoon headache. During the evening the family visited her. Shortly after, she complained of headache and was given a paracetamol tablet. Some thirty minutes later, the patient received a visit from a group of friends. The patient again complained of headache, but this time asked for aspirin. Since the second request came too soon after the first, the nurse attempted to clarify the matter. The nurse then passed on to me the patient's explanation: both tablets were intended for the water in her two bedside vases in order to increase her flowers' durability.

Can anyone help me to resolve this issue? Which of the two analgesics is more effective in prolonging the half-life of hospital flowers?

FOR years a major source of irritation on Monday mornings has been the inability of my colleague, Dr X, to arrive in time for the clinic. As a result I always have to do most of his work as well as my own. "I wish you could think of a way to get me out of bed," he often says.

A minor irritation on Monday mornings has been the regular arrival of a registered letter from a mental patient, long since discharged. But of late my small son has taken charge of this, for he loves to run downstairs in his pyjamas in answer to the postman's knock, and signing the counterfoil makes him feel important. A fortnight ago he went to boarding-school. When I found that I had to roll out of bed myself to deal with the registered letters, Monday morning became quite intolerable. Something had to be done.

Now I have solved both my problems at one brilliant stroke of the pen. I wrote to the patient the following letter:

"Dear Mrs Y, I am afraid that circumstances have changed and it will not be possible for me to receive your letters in the future. I have accordingly arranged for them to be received by Dr X at the following address . . ."

My colleague had a sour expression on his face when he arrived on Monday, just as the clinic was starting. I haven't yet dared to ask him whether the patient mentioned my name, but I think he has his suspicions.

OUR ward telephone rang the other day – it was a lady asking how Mrs Colby-Brown was getting on after her appendix operation. Sister replied that the patient was doing famously, and would shortly be sent home. Asked for her name, the lady replied: "Well, Sister, this is Mrs Colby-Brown. You're all so busy I just don't like to bother you on the ward rounds."

REQUEST on form: "Microscopy and culture of urine." Urine container empty. Diagnosis written on form: "Retention of urine."

ONE of our Commonwealth residents was interviewing the husband of an inpatient. The precise, clipped accent of the one contrasted with the broad speech of the other. "And is she eating 'owt?' inquired the anxious husband. "No," replied our young colleague, "she has all her meals in the hospital."

A DAY in the judges' tent at our local sheepdog trials started me thinking. We had booked 150 ewes to be on the field by 9 o'clock, and there they were, right on time, huddled bewildered together in the waiting-pen, uncomfortable and unsure of themselves. In another half-hour we were ready to start, with every specialist official in place. A flag was waved, stop-watches clicked, and the first three sheep were pushed out of the waiting-pen. The shepherd whistled his dog in a long sweeping arc to get behind them: they were facing the wrong way already. Eyeball to eyeball con-frontation, the stamp of one sheep forefoot, a darting feint of bared incisors by the dog to claim who should be boss, and three sheep turned straight to the line of the course. In and out of hurdle gates, round marker posts, up hill and down hill, not allowed to scatter, sometimes made to hurry, sometimes made to stand still, not a clue of what would happen next. Just unrelatable whistles and cries of "Away to me now" and "That'll do" and eight minutes' time-limit to get round the course. And then sent back to home pastures: still not quite sure what it was all about.

Next morning in hospital outpatient clinic the scene was strangely familiar. The first block bookings were there, right on time, uncomfortable and unsure of themselves. In another half-hour we were ready to start, and every specialist in place. A metaphorical flag was waved, a glance at the clock, and the first three patients were let out of the waiting-hall. Sister sent the student nurse in a long sweeping-arc to get behind them: they were facing the wrong way already. Eyeball confrontation, a flicker of resist-ance, a flash of starched apron, and three patients turned straight to the line of the course. In and out of undressing-cubicles, consulting-rooms, round sluices and X-ray markers, up stairs and down stairs, not allowed to scatter, sometimes made to hurry, sometimes made to stand still, not a clue what would happen next. Just unrelatable noises and cries of "Come with me now" and "That'll do", and an NHS time-limit to get round the course. And then sent back home: still not quite sure what it was all about. But at our sheepdog trials we also give prizes for style in handling the sheep.

ONE of the charming relics of Victorianism in medicine is the commandment: Nurses shall not speak with hospital porters. It's particularly heavily enforced in those bastions of the Establishment, the London teaching hospitals. Where I trained, however, things are made entertainingly awkward by the fact that porters and students wore the same short white jackets. My friend James tells me he was walking along the corridor in white jacket on the way to a teaching round, and was given a neighbourly good morning by a probationer nurse of his acquaintance. Suddenly, he said, everything began to happen at once. A stentorian drum-shattering shout of "NURSE!!" rang out, and the whole joint appeared to explode in a flash of light. Out of the corner of his eye James noted the green-clad Junoesque figure of the matron, and fled on the wings of the blast, but not before hearing: "Nurse, how dare you speak to that porter?"

James, a sensitive soul, was rather hurt at not being immediately taken for the consultoid material he imagined himself to consist of, but he got over it in time. He was glad to qualify, however, and to exchange his short white coat for a longer one. What happened then was, I suppose, inevitable. Admitting a patient on an unknown ward, dressed in his new long white coat, he was carrying the rectal tray to the bedside when the Sister caught sight of him. "You're late, barber" she remarked grimly. "Pubic shave number 6, please." And swept off.

Cheyne-Stokes breathing, first described in 1818, is periodic respiration associated with severe heart disease.

We were doing a ward-round when we came by an unconscious man with heavily nicotine-stained fingers, who was breathing in a curious grunting fashion, and whilst unconscious making singular repetitive movements as though he was taking his right hand to his mouth. He smoked eighty cigarettes per day and the actions suggested that he was continuing to smoke imaginary cigarettes. The registrar queried the type of respiration that the patient exhibited. Without hesitation the physician replied, "This is obviously a case of Chain-Smokers respiration."

THE cost-conscious efforts of our NHS masters regarding the reuse of items previously considered expendable after one service brings to mind a conversation I had many years ago with a theatre sister in a part of Scotland noted for its frugality. "What do you think of these new disposable gloves?" I asked. "Nae use at a'," she replied. "After ye have boiled them twice, they come back fu' o' holes."

I HAVE worked in operating-theatres as an anaesthetist for over fifty years, and experience has taught me to be very wary of nurses' questions. On one occasion a brand-new probationer nurse had been sent down by the ward sister to get her first view of a theatre in action. Having gazed all round with interest, she came up to me and said in a hoarse whisper which could be heard by everyone, "Please, Sir, may I ask you a question?" "Of course," I said, with my usual bonhomie, "what is it?" "Could you please explain why all these people wear masks except the surgeon?" Every eye was turned towards us, and the best I could think of was: "Well, he knows more about it than I do and you had better ask him."

On another occasion, a probationer had accompanied the patient from his bed to the anaesthetic room. Having injected thiopentone and sux-amethonium, and given him a few breaths of oxygen, I opened his mouth with my left hand prior to laryngoscopy. I thought that a lower incisor felt loose, and on inspection, I found it attached to a dental plate. This I removed and gave to the nurse, who took it without comment. I took up the laryngoscope again, and then the nurse said, "Can you explain something?" Rather annoyed that she had offered no apology for not preparing the patient properly, I said, somewhat ungraciously, "What is it?" "Well," she replied, "I only wanted to know why you only took out his lower plate."

# XX

# Learning from Patients

ALL in all Giles is quite sympathetic to homespun remedies. He is remarkably tolerant with patients who wear copper bangles for the relief of rheumatism; or those who carry potatoes in their pockets to alleviate arthritis. He rarely makes a comment when they enter his consulting room smelling of seaweed, tar, horse liniment, or exotic herbs. Even the erythema where a hot flat iron has been pressed on brown paper laid over an aching muscle scarcely makes him raise an eyebrow. When his patients tell him they have immersed themselves in baths of seawater, iodised soap bubbles, medicated foam, extract of sulphuretted spa water, and even thin gruel, he utters not a word. I believe he would remain silent if they said they bathed in asses' milk or vintage champagne, as long as he felt his patients were being made happy and, if not doing much good, at least the remedies were causing little harm.

His control snapped, however, when a middle-aged lady came to see him with advanced, and obviously painful, haemorrhoids. These, she said, she had been treating by applying poultices of cold tea leaves. "What is your verdict, doctor?" she asked, at the end of the examination. Giles could not restrain himself. "Well," he said, "I see a long journey over water and a tall, dark stranger will enter your life bearing gifts. As for affairs of the heart . . ."

THE morning in the operating-theatre was nearing its end. When the last patient was brought in his sterile dressings were removed and then – horror! – there was discovered, sullying the shaven and purified area of skin, a folded square of not-over-clean paper. In silence, the offence was removed and unfolded; it read: "Sir, I have a return ticket. But, in case of accidents, cheerio, all the best and thank you."

SOME time ago, I gave several of my most vocal insomniac patients each others' telephone numbers and suggested they should ring one another during the long night hours. It seemed a useful idea which might reduce the consumption of hypnotics and lead to beautiful friendships, but the Insomniacs' Club soon went into voluntary liquidation.

Mr A said he would sooner stay awake than be bored into going to sleep. Mr C's wife requested tranquillisers because, despite hanging over the bannisters half the night, she remained unconvinced of the innocence of her husband's nocturnal telephonings. Miss D resigned in a temper because persons she had phoned had twice responded with blatantly artificial snores before hanging up on her and two others retired with nervous exhaustion after accusations of cheating at telephone chess. Mr E gave up because he felt he could stay awake quite well without the help of having to worry about how to pay his phone bill. This was partly due to Mr F, who would transfer the charge and then fall asleep without replacing his receiver.

One of the last to leave the club was old Mr Y, whose wife phoned me at 3 in the morning and asked me to listen. "What's he sawing wood for at this hour?" I asked. "It'd be quieter if he was! That's him snoring! For richer, for poorer, for better for worse, is fair enough, but the contract said nothing about sound-effects." I said I thought he had insomnia. "So he had, and you give it him right back or I'll sue you!"

MY chatty but breathless patient was discharged from the ward to await the results of her avian precipitins test. This came back positive for budgerigars and I informed her GP. When I saw her again a few weeks later I started, "I hope you are glad that we seem to have found the cause of your trouble." "Oh yes! I'm much better thank you, doctor," she replied, "but I must tell you. When I was pretty bad at home, the vicar prayed for me in church one Sunday morning and do you know, doctor, that very afternoon my budgie died."

God may move in a mysterious way, but He certainly gets there.

A PATIENT of mine needed a short series of tests for occult blood and the specimens were being dutifully carried from home to laboratory by her husband. "He makes a wonderful stool pigeon," she said.

I AM not going to write about tattoos. The subject merits nothing less than an entire special number of *The Lancet*, with articles on the Histopathology of Tattooing, the Psychology of the Tattooed, Tattoos and Social Medicine, and so forth. I merely want to submit an interesting case – more interesting, I think, than the not uncommon row of blue dots across the root of the neck with "Cut Along The Dotted Line" above them: certainly more so than the quite frequent "I Love Mary" altered to an indelible declaration of affection for Katie. This tattoo was a hunt in full cry. The scene began at the umbilicus with a line of pink-coated horsemen galloping towards the right shoulder – all executed with a skilful impression of the dash and vigour of the chase. The meet continued on to the back, the hounds having got ahead as far as the spine of the scapula. The pack filled the remaining space as far as the buttocks, where the fox's brush could be seen disappearing into the anus. The tableau was labelled, sure enough, "Gone to Earth".

THE man in dungarees who entered the casualty department was asked why he had come. "I've got the gravel," he replied. He was asked to wait behind the screen in a cubicle. Five minutes later a doctor went in to get the history. "What is this you were saying about gravel?" "It's in my lorry outside. Where am I supposed to put it?"

ONE useful tip I had picked up from my lately retired senior partner was "always turn out to babies", so when I got a call at 2 in the morning from the mother of a nine-month-old baby I set out at once. I examined her offspring from top to toe and finding only a temperature decided that he had an upper-respiratory infection and required only nursing. I explained all this to her and she said, "As a matter of fact I thought that was what you would say, doctor. I had the same trouble with my six-year-old when he was this age. I rang old Dr Black and he was able to tell me over the telephone that all would be well until he could come in the morning. Of course," she added, "he would be more experienced than you, doctor, wouldn't he?"

THE tendency to send cards or gifts seems to be compulsive at this season, so I was surprised to note a modest discomfiture as the penultimate patient of the morning clinic delved awkwardly into her shopping-bag and eventually produced a carton wrapped in crumpled "Christmas Greetings" paper. I was more than usually effusive in my thanks. Perhaps because of her youth, or possibly because she was one of my most conspicuous therapeutic failures, and had suffered so much fruitless discomfort at my hands, I protested how unnecessary was her generosity, and disclaimed all her attempts – as I thought – to sing my praises. My curiosity got the better of me and I could not wait to finish my clinic before opening the parcel. This was just as well, as it enabled the duty nurse to test the specimen of urine before lunch.

THERE is an air of embarrassment in the unit just now. Our registrar, the clever one, instead of bombarding the chief with unheard-of syndromes named after unpronounceable Slavs, is holding his place meekly at second from the end in the ward-round queue. I am sure the chief thinks he has gone on holiday.

The trouble started when one of that fast-fading clan – the gentlemen of the road – was admitted on the verge of diabetic coma. A known diabetic he carried a grubby card which gave his insulin requirements and a few other particulars. In a paper-wrapped bundle, along with some other oddments, lay his syringe and needles. He admitted that he had been a bit irregular with his injections of late but as it hadn't interfered with his appetite he hadn't bothered. He obviously had not washed for weeks.

Our registrar asked him what methods of insulin administration were employed by those for whom a regular toilet was an unpleasant thought rather than a happy action. Our patient laughed at the thought of cleansing his skin before giving himself a "sticker". He injected himself through his trouser leg like everybody else did, he supposed. It was dead easy and it hadn't done him any harm yet. Sure enough, the thighs, while dirt-encrusted, were free from scars.

Pale with horror, our registrar, like a missionary in an alien clime, lectured him on the error of such ways. He pointed out the dangers, the complications, the ills, and the miseries that ignorance would bring. With his own hands, he decided, he would demonstrate how an injection should be given. After several minutes of hard work the skin was clean. The syringe carefully sterilised, the correct amount of insulin was measured, and the area injected in the approved painless way.

The tramp, despite the registrar's careful commentary, was, on the whole, not impressed. He was even less impressed two days later, when the abscess began to form.

"My lodger," said Mrs Brown, "is rather a vague type. When he didn't come down one morning I looked in on him and he said he felt ill, so I called the doctor who diagnosed tonsillitis, put him on the usual tablets, ordered a fluid diet, and asked for a specimen. The patient said he'd like a cup of weak milky tea, so I took one up to him and also a bottle for the specimen. Next time I went up the tea was gone but he hadn't done anything about the specimen, so I took one from the jerry and sent it up to the doctor. Half an hour later he was on the telephone to say that he was sending an ambulance to take my lodger into hospital because he had serious kidney disease and what was the name and address of his next-of-kin? Well, we sent the lodger off in the ambulance but two days later he walked in quite well again. Well, of course, what happened was that he had taken against the tea after the first mouthful and poured the rest into the jerry, so the specimen I sent up was full of albumin, don't you call it?"

"Did he take sugar in his tea?" I asked. "No," said Mrs Brown. "A good thing," I said. "He might have had diabetes as well."

"The trouble with you," said my Most Difficult Patient, "is that you're a political doctor." I expressed mild surprise and inquired what he meant. "Ah," he said, "remember when you first came to see me, four years ago?" I did vaguely recall the occasion. "Then you told me to stay in bed for a week," he continued, "but I knew better and went back to work. But after –" here he paused significantly, "after, when you came to see me, you told me to get up and go back to work." "After what?" I asked. "After the Tories came into power, that's what; I said you were a political doctor," was the triumphant reply.

WE are often told that we must keep the patient informed about his condition. But my double role as hospital specialist and anonymous medical correspondent of a popular magazine has brought home to me that what really matters is not what we say, but what the patient understands.

A patient of mine had occupied far more than the ordinary quota of outpatient time. With considerable care, using many homely metaphors, I had explained the mechanism of the origin and persistence of her symptoms; she seemed to have grasped the position. A few days later in my postbag at the magazine I found a letter . . . If it had not been for the name and postal district, I would hardly have guessed it was the same patient. All ended well, however, because the magazine doctor was able to clear up the misunderstanding left by the hospital chump.

ONE has to be so careful of one's phraseology when assessing fitness for anaesthesia. "Are your teeth your own?" "Yes, doctor." No doubt they were: when, a few minutes later, we fished them out of his pharaynx on the end of an airway we realised that he must have finished paying for them.

WHEN the chief said we were to get blood-alcohols on every patient who had been involved in a road accident, I thought it was an interesting idea; but I lost some of my enthusiasm, and some of my faith in our lab's dexterity in the estimation of blood-alcohol, when the highest level we got was from an eminently sober Nonconformist minister who was knocked off his bicycle on his way from one chapel to another. I was quite alarmed at the thought that some legal issue might depend on one of our blood-alcohol levels when one man whose permission I asked to draw blood for the estimation said, "Sure, take it and let me know the answer. If there's none there, I'll sue the pub."

HOW few of my medical patients behave sensibly when they have their coronaries. One doctor was being driven home from dinner by his wife when he suddenly said, "Stop the car and let me out", at which he leapt out and ran off down the road into the dark. A few minutes later he breathlessly approached the car from the opposite direction, fell into his seat, and said, "Well, that's all right." "What on earth did you do that for?" asked his bemused wife, to which he replied, "Well, I had an awful pain in my chest and I did not know whether it was a coronary or indigestion. I thought that if I ran and it was a coronary it should have got worse, but I've run round the block and it hasn't so it must be indigestion."

MY favourite neurotic has a naive charm which is irresistible. No matter how frequent and unjustified her requests for visits, I cannot help but like her. Her latest comment is typical: "There's something wrong with my neighbour. She never has the doctor in."

HE was a welcome change from the succession of dreary souls with faces as long as their list of symptoms, and tempers as irritable as their colons; and my heart warmed to his cheery face and twinkling eye as he puffed in medical outpatients. My surgical colleagues had obviously felt the same way about him, for they hoped that we would relieve his bronchial spasm as successfully as they had his retention.

Having duly percussed and listened, I was about to prescribe an antispasmodic and an expectorant when it struck me that his GP might already be giving him something of the sort. To my question he replied that his doctor prescribed a medicine, three times a day; a small pill, twice a day; an inhalation, one a day; and a linctus for the night.

"And do they help you?" I asked, thwarted. "Oh, I don't ever take them," he replied. "But you won't write and tell him that will you? It might hurt his feelings. You see, he is a fine doctor, and I have great faith in him."

"It's the camshaft," the tester said after two minutes on the road with my aged Rover. "Is it serious?" I asked anxiously, knowing as little about a camshaft as he knows about the islets of Langerhans. There followed a brief dissertation on prognosis and treatment. It was only the next day that the thought struck me: what had happened to the camshaft? was it broken, bent, or missing? I hadn't asked the vital question. In what way, I asked myself, was I different from the patient who says "it's my heart" or "it's my liver", without having bothered to ask what had gone wrong.

I HAVE just finished examining our local gym teacher. He had been a combat instructor in the Forces before leaving to take up his new appointment in the old school down the road. Although a strict disciplinarian, his toughness and physical fitness won him the respect of pupils and colleagues alike. He has just asked me to certify that the balance of his mind is disturbed and that he is not responsible for his actions.

Apparently he had been taking a particularly unruly class and in order to control one youth, wilder than the others, he had eventually resorted to that familiar instrument, the leather strap. The boy left the class in high dudgeon, threatening that his father would call immediately to sort him out. My patient was understandably upset and sought the advice of his headmaster. That individual suggested the best thing to do would be to take a week's leave immediately. The boy's father was a notorious local hard man.

He returned to his work more than a little disturbed. That afternoon, in the middle of a class, the door burst open and a large man entered the gym, taking off his jacket as he came. The janitor followed hot on his heels. Believing, of course, that attack was the best defence, my patient ran to meet him and, without a word, knocked him flat with a right to the jaw. As the man collapsed at his feet, the janitor let out a yell of horror. "What have you done to the clerk of works?" he cried. "He was only here to mend the windows."

# XXI

# Miscellany

IT may seem odd that in such a healthy place as a university I have already been called to five different people in coma this term. The classic cases of age-group were all included: a faint, an epileptic fit, and a boy "dead-drunk" on British wine. Then there was the sudden death of an older man with a violent cerebrovascular accident. The fifth case presented a much greater difficulty in diagnosis, and it reminded me of Sir Boyle Roche's remark in the House of Commons: "Mr Speaker, I smell a rat. I see him forming in the air and darkening the sky! But I'll nip him in the bud." She was a first-year student and had been walking down the road for a 9 o'clock lecture. She stepped straight off the pavement into the path of a motorcycle. She did not seem to be too severely injured, although she did suffer a large bruise on her right thigh and a graze on her right hand. She was able to proceed to her lecture, but I think she must have been a "bit dazed" – as she put it – for she noticed she was not taking any lecture notes. About half-way through the lecture she suddenly saw a large brown rat with a long tail, at the front of the lecture theatre. The girl sitting beside her had seen nothing and so a violent reaction was precipitated. She started to giggle, then to weep, and had to be escorted from the room in a state of collapse. When I examined her immediately afterwards I could find no neurological explanation for this hallucination. A series of differential diagnoses came to mind. My immediate reaction was to consider LSD as a powerful hallucinogen; this too could explain her carelessness on the roadside. Temporal-lobe epilepsy was another possibility; head injury or delayed shock could not be ruled out. She was, however, recovering fairly rapidly and I delayed further investigation until the traditional cup of tea had had time to work. The true diagnosis was revealed some forty minutes later in a telephone call from the lecturer. He had just killed a large rat in the lecture room. It had reappeared and then run to its doom behind the blackboard. It turned out later that several other students in the lecture theatre had seen the rat, but none had cared to mention it.

MY colleague was fed up with training receptionists, employing them for a short time, and then saying farewell as they got wed and pregnant in rapid succession. Next time he played safe and took on a well-documented grandmother. But he'd forgotten that they marry very young in that part of the city, and last week she gave in her notice . . .

I HAVE stopped smoking cigarettes. How smug I am. Nobody dislikes me more than me too. There are no compensations. My singing voice has improved, but then I could not sing a note in key before, so the only effect is that my bathroom voice penetrates more piercingly into the privacy of my musically minded family. My breathing also is freer. Great lumps of lovely fresh air sweep down into alveoli that have been smoked filled for years. So, also, do large dollops of the metropolitan atmospheric cocktail of diesel oil and smog. My squash rackets has improved of course, but in any case I am too old to be playing the game at all, and the extra effort that I can now put into it must be taxing my coronaries to the limit.

Appreciation of good food and wine is a long-forgotten and now renewed delight; particularly to my tailor, who has done all that safety and decency permits in the way of letting out, and now with undisguised enthusiasm embarks upon a new sartorial building programme.

Actually, this stopping of cigarettes has not been too bad – I have taken the edge off the misery by an occasional cigar. Being inexperienced, I have not always been inspired in my selection of cigars, and if during one of the inevitable attacks of vertigo which accompany an unfortunate choice I should fall under a bus I do hope I live long enough to laugh at the clever way in which I have avoided a lung tumour.

THE best salesman I ever encountered was a hospital gardener who bred pedigree dogs as a supplementary source of income. When a family appeared to buy a pup, the litter was quickly designated. Two were called "show" dogs, one was the "runt" and the rest were referred to simply as "pets". The price was scaled accordingly. At the viewing, the gardener let it be known that he thought an ordinary house pet would meet their needs. A show dog was not really for the likes of them. This repeated remark invariably made the father buy the most expensive animal available. Eventually only two were left: the runt and one destined for Crufts. By using the same inverted snob technique, the latter was easily disposed of. The last of the litter was freely admitted to be not fit for showing. However, he said, it had such a lovable personality that his wife had demanded it for herself. He could only let it go for an enhanced sum. The pup's attractive character was emphasised by the way it scampered forward to lick his fingers when he appeared (they had previously been dipped in honey). No child could resist it.

His spiritual colleague was a senior consultant when I was but a medical pup myself. One day, through a series of misunderstandings, he removed a small boy's tonsils and adenoids instead of the hernia for which the child had been admitted. Panic ran through the administrative block, but the great man was unruffled. Leave it to me, he said. He met the lad's father and after a short time they parted, with the parent shaking him by the hand, thanking him profusely and swearing he would not say a thing to a soul. "How did you do it?" asked the hospital secretary. "Quite simply," replied the surgeon. "I told him that when I examined the child, his tonsils and adenoids were so bad that they had to come out at once. I insisted he be put at the top of the year long waiting list but, by jumping the queue as I did, I was placed in a difficult position with my colleagues – and heaven only knows what would happen if those on the waiting list ever found out. I will, of course, repair the hernia in a few months' time." Pups and tonsils, it's all in how you do it.

ONCE upon a time there was another little boy who had a bicycle, which he artfully sabotaged. Thus, when it broke down, which was usually, he had an excuse for being late for school, while the bicycle chain, when removed and lashed on to nine inches of broom-handle, was of assistance during financial discussions with his little playmates.

One day as he was replacing the handle-bars back to front, a passing Psychiatrist, realising that both boy and bicycle were maladjusted, stopped and repaired the machine. "There you are, little boy," he said, "Your bicycle is now un-maladjusted and will get you to school on time every morning. On each of your half-holidays you must bring it to me for an overhaul, while you yourself attend for treatment at a bicycle shop, for I observe that you are emotionally disequilibriated, maladjusted, and a victim of diminished responsibility."

"You gimme that in writing, Daddy-O?" asked the little boy with the first show of interest that afternoon. "Certainly," replied the Psychiatrist, signing a certificate to that effect. This the little boy put carefully into his pocket. He then mounted his bicycle and re-maladjusted it by knocking down the Psychiatrist and killing him.

And they all – excepting of course the Psychiatrist – lived happily ever after. And that's why psychiatrists are called trick-cyclists.

WHAT, we often hear asked, constitutes consultant status? One of many factors is a man's own view of himself. There is a famous pair of photographs in the residents' dining-room at a certain teaching hospital. The October group shows the mess, including a tousle-haired smiling youth with baggy trousers who signs himself "Alf Smith". There they all are again, the following April, except for our friend, who at first sight seems to have left. But who is this splendid creature, with the immaculate parting and the pin-stripe suit, the heavy spectacles, the heavier countenance? The signature reads "A. B. Champion-Smith". Good Heavens, it's old Alf!

I HAVE always had doubts about the efficiency of postal follow-ups, and my misgivings were reinforced when a patient with a thrice recurrent hernia told me that his secretary had answered the inquiry from his previous surgeon (which came while he was in hospital) by reporting him as well and free from recurrence for fear of giving offence to "such a nice man".

OUR family tour through Italy was delightful but I did just wonder about the impact of all those Florentine statues on the minds of our overdressed children. Our daughter, aged 10, contemplated Michaelangelo's David from all sides and then came up with the breathless announcement, "What fingernails! What fingernails!" I checked. She was right, there were fingernails. That there was more than fingernails, however, emerged when we came home and had all our photographs developed. From her camera came a picture of Fenton (age 6) posing as David on a Florentine veranda.

THE senior surgeon tossed me the bundle of applications for the post of additional consultant surgeon. I spent hours arranging them in order of merit. He brushed my list aside, and searching through the referees' names, asked his secretary to ring two of them. As luck would have it, he had spoken to both within five minutes. "That's my lad," he said, indicating the name of a referee on the back of a form. "You don't even know the candidate's name," I said. "Nonsense, he's called Bill, and he plays hockey." I turned over the sheet and confirmed this, but he was low in my league table. "He's got his fellowship, and he's been a senior registrar," retorted the senior surgeon. "Anyway, you can't talk. You were recommended to me over a nightcap, and for three reasons. You were easy to get on with, you didn't mind hard work, and your wife's preoccupation with the cost of living was undermining your whole-time zeal for abstruse research." "I don't see the point of my last qualification." "Very important. Your wife did not like penury, and she had some influence over you. She has since chosen a beautiful house with a magnificent mortgage and is happy here; so you won't move. Steady undisturbed work is what I want on my unit."

Extract from medical report form for one of the Big Five banks:
"For colour vision, ability to distinguish between RED and BLACK is the only requirement."

THE designations on the doors in our department are made up from plastic letters which are attached to the doors with small nails. When the doors were painted a few months ago the letters were removed. The letters on the gentlemen's lavatory were, for some unknown reason, not replaced. They were left loose on the shelf above the urinal. Since then one has become accustomed to seeing a fresh arrangement of letters on almost every visit – obviously the work of an idle hand. When all the permutations and combinations of the nine letters had been made, judicious breaking of one or more of them widened the vocabulary considerably.

Why don't local authorities try placing a selection of letters at convenient positions in all public lavatories, so that compulsive word-makers may satisfy themselves, and possibly others, by their efforts, without having recourse to the walls? If the idea caught on, I'm sure the mental stimulus of a visit to a lavatory thus equipped would benefit a lot of people. I must say I enjoy a quick game of single-handed scrabble.

ACCORDING to the guidebook, the river at Galway is so stuffed with salmon during the spring run that you can't see the riverbed. The uppermost of the bridges is the spot designated for this sight, and so we wandered down hopefully. Not a fish could be seen. I asked a local man if the spring run was on. "Yes," he said, "they have started to come up; only a few as yet because too much water is coming down. But now the weather will be fine and in a day or two there will be thousands." So back we went on the next day: still no fish in view. An old man sidled up to me as I gazed over the parapet. "See any?" he asked cautiously. "Not one," I replied. "Ah," he said, "there is too much water coming down. Now yesterday there were thousands. But the weather will be fine, and in the next day or two . . ."

I conclude that the bit in the guidebook was written by an Irishman.

Just about the commonest complaint heard from the active consultant is the impossibility of keeping up with the vast range of publications which purport to cover even the smallest of our specialties. I am certainly not alone in having often expressed the wish that I lived in more gracious times, when not only was there much less to read but also more leisure in which to cover it. A few weeks ago I had occasion to consult Thomas Hodgkin's article in which he first described the condition which now bears his name. I took myself off to the library of our local Royal College of Physicians to get the *Transactions of the Medico-Chirurgical Society of London* for 1832, only to discover that the pages were uncut. Dismissing this as a chance event, I then borrowed from the university library the *Guy's Hospital Reports* for the year when Hodgkin's name was first given to the disease by Wilks, and again I was confronted by uncut pages. Does this mean that our assumptions have been wrong and that our forefathers did not have time to read as the pace of life was even more hectic than today? Or does it mean that covering the literature was less important for the membership candidate of the 19th century? I feel, however, that neither of these explanations is the right one, and that in truth the pages were uncut because of the well-known habit of the Scot of refusing to concede that anything of value ever came from an institution south of the border.

We have all known a patient who carried out our instructions too literally, and it is nice to know that other professions have the same difficulties. Many years ago I heard of a child who was asked in an examination what he must do to obtain forgiveness of sin, and who replied that first he must sin. More recently I encountered a lecturer in methods of education who always impressed on his students the importance of making themselves crystal-clear when telling children what to do. While giving a demonstration lesson he noticed a child chewing gum; he pointed a finger at the offender and then gestured towards the waste-paper basket. The child didn't move and again the admonitory finger pointed first at him and then at the basket. Finally comprehension dawned – the child came to the front of the classroom and stood in the waste-paper basket. The students were very impressed.

THOSE of us who are monoglot are in a weak position for making jokes about other people's use of language, but everyone has his own favourite tale. I put forward for trumping by fellow peripatetics the moment in the 17th International Congress on Occupational Health when what the speaker described as "an emergency care ambulance" was translated as "a mobile salvation unit".

IT all began with an overdraft. Something had to be done at once; or at least that's what our bank manager said. I remembered a diamond brooch, left by my grandmother, lying discarded in a drawer with some old cosmetics. This, I decided, should be our salvation. So I set out for London, bearing also a seed-pearl necklace for good measure. My first stop was a large jeweller's where my name and address were taken and the brooch was put in an envelope. An immediate offer? Impossible, I was told. I mumbled an excuse, seized the envelope, and withdrew. On to a world-famous art dealer, where I am informed I'd be lucky to get a quarter of the value estimated for insurance. I say it would pay me to have the burglars in: we part on a chilly note. Finally, to Hatton Garden. Here, gaining entry was a bit of an ordeal. First one ring – then a buzz – door opens. Second door appears – another buzz – door opens. Finally I come face to face with a small man who eyes me without curiosity. How much do I want for it? As much as I can get, I reply. He offers rather less than half the insurance value. I ask if I may telephone my husband. Certainly, he says; but first I must allow him to seal the brooch in an envelope with the offered figure written across the seal. The offer stands only so long as the envelope is returned with the seal unbroken – in other words, he is not going to be beaten up by a counter-bid a pound or two better. My husband proves to be out. So, feeling a bit of a fool, I say I need the money badly; will he unseal the envelope and buy the brooch? While the cheque is being completed I hopefully produce the seed pearls. As the jeweller lets these trickle through his fingers he murmurs something about people in the East grinding them up and eating them. Back home I learn that my husband has that day bought his first new suit in three years – which is fine but puts our finances back where they were. Any bids for a valuable seed-pearl necklace in mint, unchewed condition?

MY mother used to describe the first meal she ever made for my grandmother, her mother-in-law. It was a traditional high tea. For those not familiar with the repast, this consists of a main course, bread, confectionery, and a great deal of tea. My grandmother was a most particular lady and this first meal was something of a test piece. Both knew it.

My mother laboured long and hard; and in the end she was satisfied. Apart from the main course, which would be cooked under my grandmother's watchful eye, the table was set. There was white bread, brown bread, and currant bread; sugar scones, treacle scones, and raisin scones; six varieties of biscuit; there were rhubarb tarts, apple tarts, and mixed fruit tarts; seed cake, cherry cake, and sultana cake; six sorts of small cake, iced and plain; there was shortbread, gingerbread, and sugar puffs; double-cream layer cake, chocolate cake, and a jam sponge; there was butter, margarine, and six types of jam. There was a pot of honey. Mother-in-law slowly surveyed the laden table. "What a pity," she said at last, "that you don't have a plain white scone. If there is one thing I like, it is a plain white scone."

A friend of my wife's had a somewhat similar experience but in reverse, when her son invited his new girl friend for dinner. Mother's speciality was Hungarian goulash with all the appropriate side-dishes and this was duly served. After referring to the ingredients and the problems of proportion, she expressed the hope that the young lady would like it. "Don't worry," replied the girl friend, "I can eat anything as long as there is tomato sauce." I sometimes think only the arrival of an obstetrician can bridge gaps of such immensities.

IT will come as no surprise to readers of *The Lancet* to hear examples of its diagnostic value. Taking for granted, however, all the high-powered technology, there is also the subject of the actual printed journal. An ophthalmologist friend tells me that his medically qualified patients often quote inability to read *The Lancet* in a moving railway train as a first sign of hypermetropia. In this situation, it leaves its competitors standing.

IF you want to stir up the local populace just a little, plan a psychiatric hostel in the community. To ruffle them somewhat more, make it a hostel for the mentally retarded. But, I have discovered, if you really want to get them going, plan a small community home for the elderly severely mentally infirm (an ESMI unit, to use the jargon), for there is something about the elderly that really puts up the backs of the locals, and if the old people are mad as well . . .

We were foolish enough to plan just such a unit. There was this large Victorian house, going at a reasonable price; as part of a package deal for the closure of an old and inconvenient ex-workhouse hospital, the Health Authority were willing to purchase. The house was the sole survivor in the road, its contemporaries having been flattened long ago, several modern dwellings rising upon each site. The occupants of these, once the news leaked out, formed a Residents' Association which promptly set about fighting our proposals, quoting such apparently relevant facts as "We have wives and daughters, you know" as the reasons for opposition.

Eventually, after much effort, we obtained planning permission and the unit was duly opened. With much care and tact on our part we managed to establish an uneasy *modus vivendi* with the locals, and eventually the shining new door-chains with which every house had been equipped fell into disuse.

Peaceful coexistence was threatened by the unit cat. Mindful of the benefits to the elderly from a pet around the house, Sister had acquired a pretty tortoiseshell kitten. Too late we discovered her (the cat, not Sister) to be virtually feral, and not at all disposed to be a cuddly, strokable lap-cat. Despite being well fed, she believed in supplementing her official rations with the fauna of the neighbourhood; this might not have caused problems, were it not that (a) her proclivities became common knowledge and (b) our immediate neighbour, the chairman of the Residents' Association, kept racing pigeons.

Sister and I conducted the postmortem in the sluice. There was no doubt, scanty though the remains were, that it had been a pigeon. Moreover, the noise of grain being rattled in a tin next door led us to believe that one of the flock was posted AWOL. Also there was little doubt of the guilty party, sitting washing her blood-stained whiskers with the trouble-free conscience that only a lifetime of evil can bring.

Sister rose to the occasion. Taking the ring from the bird's leg, she announced she would send it to her nephew and ask him to post it back, saying he had found the bird, dead of exhaustion, in his garden. The ploy worked, and our neighbour's grief at losing his champion bird has been tinged with pride at its remarkable stamina. I had not realised that Sister's nephew works in Dubai.

One evening last week I saw the Perfect Commercial. The scene was the last stage of a gracious dinner-party. The hostess muttered something about coffee and withdrew to the adjacent kitchen where, while making hissing and spluttering noises like a percolator in action, she ladled granules from a jar of instant coffee into the glass receptacle and added the boiling water. When she handed a cup of the fluid to her guest, did the latter go into the all-too-familiar ecstasies, demanding to know the secret of such excellence and thus cueing her hostess into the expected rigmarole about the coffee beans having been hand-picked and expertly blended under laboratory conditions to preserve their unique aroma, and provoking a chorus of agreement from the rest of the assemblage? No, she did not. She took a sip: her face lit up with surprise and delight: she just murmured, "What lovely coffee", and resumed her lively colloquy with her neighbour. The whole episode was a cameo, some fifteen seconds of Real Life, contrasting with that fantasy world whose inhabitants grimace and over-react noisily when confronted with some new product. The sad thing was that I did not notice the name of the brand.

It is always the same. I adore the chimpanzees' tea-party and rate it as one of the highest spots on ITV, but I still can't remember which brand of tea they are advertising. I am a compulsive commercial-watcher, but to the best of my knowledge I have never been conned into buying anything I would not otherwise have bought. I would, however, have liked in my small way to swell the profits of the firm who had the nous to engage the script-writer and producer of this little masterpiece. And the same goes for the chimpanzees' backers.

Should professional actors participate in commercials? My reaction when I see someone I recognise is one of pity. "Poor chap," I think, "Is he so hard up that he has to prostitute his talent in this way, saying something he's been instructed to say, when he doesn't believe a word of it?" An actor friend of mine could not see it that way. In the theatre, he said, when playing Tartuffe or Malvolio, he often had to utter sentiments, written for him, which he himself did not hold. It came to the same thing. In a commercial he was paid to enact someone wildly enthusiastic about something or other, and it didn't matter what. If the undiscerning public identified him as Tartuffe or Malvolio or an after-shave addict, so much the better. We agreed to differ.

FROM an explanatory notice in Bergen aquarium – "The octopus belongs to the molluscs and was perfected some millions of years ago. The octopus is one of the most intelligent and able animals in the sea. Its eye is another sublime solution and can compete with the eyes of vertebrates. With some slight alterations the octopus could have become the ruler of the world."

FINGERNAILS on the menu again at Cockaignshire County Hall, where the executive council is hearing Mrs A's complaints, or at least the first half-dozen or so, against Dr X for downright ignorance when dealing with her obesity.

Four-foot-ten Mrs A, who tips the scale at twenty-two stone and has no difficulty in making the weight, was getting the bad news from a British Railways weighing-machine she had discovered behind the 2nd-class refreshment rooms (where the porters hide when they hear a train coming) when she noticed that the instrument bore a chart giving average weights for height and age. Simple extrapolation of these data revealed that, with her weight and age, she should be eight feet tall, and she therefore claims to be in fact a dwarf and that Dr X should have treated her for vertical undergrowth rather than for circumferential overgrowth. Also the machine, in its death-throes, bequeathed to Mrs A a little card. On one side was printed her weight, followed by the interjection COR!; and on the other side it said she was born under the zodiacal sign Scorpio, was easily put-upon because of her trusting nature, lucky stone the carbuncle.

Mrs A told the council she had always had carbuncles and come to think